NORMAN CARLISLE

RICHES of the SEA
The NEW SCIENCE of OCEANOLOGY

PHOENIX
HOUSE

OTHER BOOKS OF INTEREST

from Phoenix House

MEN UNDER THE SEA   Egon Larsen
WEALTH FROM THE OCEANS   Tony Loftas
LIFE IN THE DEEP   Maurice Burton

PICTURE CREDITS

The author and publisher wish to thank the following organizations for black-and-white pictures which they supplied. The following symbols are used in this list: top (t); bottom (b); right (r); left (l); center (c).

Aqua-Chem, Inc., 90 b; Arabian American Oil Co., 73 t, 76 b, 77 t; Autonetics, 124; N. W. Ayer & Son, Inc., 11 b, 62, 63; Barkin, Herman and Associates, 89, 91 c, 91 b; Bechtel Corp., 91 t; Brookhaven National Laboratories, 60; Brown & Root, 78, 79, 80, 81, 82; Bureau of Mines (Tiburon), 10 b; Department of Fisheries, Canada, 50, 58 t, 59; Dow Chemical Company, 85, 86, 87, 88; EG & G International, Inc., 12 t, 30, 37 t, b, 38, 39 b, 40 t, b, 41, 44 tl, bl, 45; Embassy of the U.S.S.R., 100, 101, 102; Environmental Science Service Administration (ESSA), 103, 104, 111; Freeport Sulphur Co., 67, 68 t, 70 t; French Embassy Press & Information Division, 12 b; 31 t, b, 96, 97, 98, 99, 114 b, 119; General Dynamics Corp., 13 b, 14 b, 24, 26 t, b, 106, 116 b; 118; General Electric Co., 125; General Motors Corp., 6; Grumman Aircraft Co., 29; Gulf Oil Co., 13 t, 73 b, 74 t; Hewlett-Packard Co., 44 br; Hughes Aircraft Co., 123; Lockheed-California Co., 39 t, 44 tr, 46, 69 t; Lockheed Missiles & Space Co., 27 t, 28; Martin Company, 105, 115; Mobil Oil Corp., 8 b, 9 t, 72, 74 b; Natick Laboratories, U.S. Army, 58 b; Oak Ridge National Laboratories, 9 b, 94 b; Ocean Systems, 7, 32 b, 33; Office of Saline Water, 90 t, 92, 93, 94 t; Official Photograph U.S. Navy, 5, 10 t, 15 t, b, 17, 19, 20, 21, 23, 32 t, 42 b, 43, 49, 120, 121, 122; Radio Corp. of America, 42 t, 47 b, 51, 52; Reynolds Aluminum Co., 22, 25; Standard Oil Company of California, 75, 76 tl, tr; Standard Oil Company of New Jersey, 8 t, 14 t, 77 b; Sun Shipbuilding & Dry Dock Co., 27 b; University of California at San Diego (UCSD) Scripps Institute, 113, 114 t, 116 t; University of California, San Diego, 47 t, 48, 61, 84; U.S. Bureau of Mines, 3, 64, 65, 66, 68 b, 69 b, 70 b; U.S. Coast & Geodetic Survey, 112; U.S. Coast Guard, 107, 109, 110; U.S. Department of the Interior, 53, 54, 55, 56, 57, 95; U.S. Weather Bureau, 117; Westinghouse Electric Corp., 11 t, 34, 36, 71.

The author and publisher also wish to thank the following for the use of the color photographs used in this book: Aqua-Chem, Inc., H; Autonetics Division of North American Aviation Inc., D; EG & G International, Inc., E–t; Freeport Sulphur Co., G–b, G–t; General Electric Co., B–b; Grumman Aircraft Corp., B–t; Lockheed Missiles & Space Co., C–b; Pan American Petroleum Corp., F–t; Reynolds Aluminum Co., E–b; Sun Shipbuilding Corp., C–t; U. S. Navy Electronics Laboratory, F–b; W. J. Voit Rubber Corp., A–b; Westinghouse Electric Corp., A–t.

A device for taking mineral samples is lowered into the sea.

CONTENTS

An artist's drawing depicts depths reached by various manned devices. The pressure figures are given in tons per square inch.

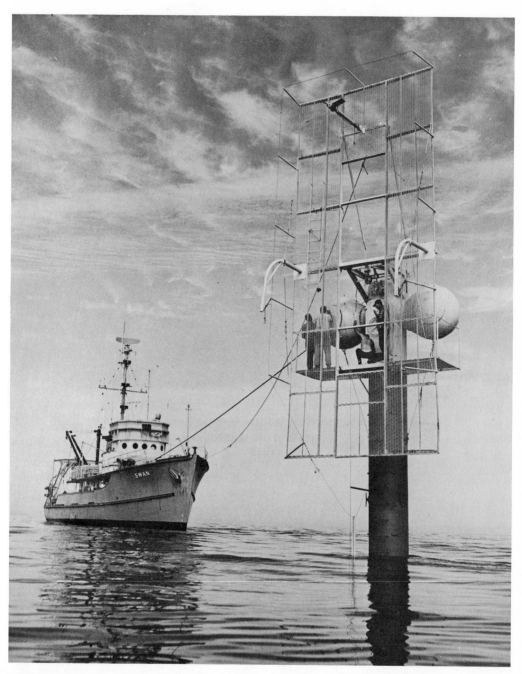

POP (Perpendicular Ocean Platform) is useful in all phases of oceanographic research. Here POP is being set up in its vertical position. A portable lab will be installed on the grid platform.

I. RICHES OF THE SEA

The fishermen aboard a ship watch the television screen intently. At just the right moment, one of them pushes a switch. Below, a school of fish swimming through the cold waters of the Atlantic suddenly feel a tingle of electricity. The fish change course, rushing straight into the mouth of a huge net.

*   *   *

A strange dredge moves slowly across the water off the southwest coast of Africa. A conveyor belt comes up out of the sea, covered with gravel. Machinery aboard the dredge sifts out the mud and silt from the treasure being sought—diamonds from the sea.

*   *   *

On the west coast of the U.S., water is

Jon Lindbergh, underwater pioneer, shown in a one-man submarine designed by Ocean Systems for work on the Continental Shelf.

pouring into the mains, headed for southern California's thirsty cities. The water comes from the first giant nuclear power plant that can turn salt-laden sea water into drinkable fresh water.

*   *   *

In the North Sea, on an acre-sized man-made island of steel, a sudden roar rises above the din of machinery. The men on the platform shout in triumph. Their drills have struck natural gas.

*   *   *

In a long, low structure on the estuary of France's River Rance, submarine-like turbines begin to hum. Electricity from them surges into the national power grid. For the first time in history man is lighting a city with power from the sea.

*   *   *

These are just a few of the ways in which science and technology have joined forces to create the new science of oceanology. For the first time man is making an organized, scientific effort to tap the riches and powers of "inner space," the World Ocean that covers more than 70 per cent of the surface of our globe.

A challenge to science

Just a few years ago man was content to use the seas as highways for ships and a hunting ground for a few species of fish. Now all that is changed.

"Man must turn to the seas at last," says Columbus O'Donnell Iselin, noted oceanographer of the Woods Hole Oceanographic Institute in Massachusetts. "Only in the oceans can we find enough food, minerals, and water to meet pressing world needs."

Statements like this have long been made by far-seeing ocean scientists, but only in the 1960's did a soaring world population and

7

"*Ocean Traveller*," a floating drilling rig, was towed across the Atlantic from New Orleans, where it was built, to this site in the North Sea.

a growing scarcity of raw materials spur the mighty organized effort now underway. Today, science, engineering, industry and government are working together to explore our last frontier.

The United States, Great Britain, Canada, Japan, the U.S.S.R., the Scandinavian countries—all are expanding ocean research. The U.S. alone has a $2,300,000,000 budget for sea research in the next decade, a figure matched by the expenditures of private industry as dozens of the biggest U.S. corporations plunge into oceanology.

The challenge of food

With world population already over 3,000,000,000 and destined to climb to double that figure by the year 2000, all experts agree that the spectre of famine stalks our planet. In India alone, in the next decade, 50,000,000

A scuba diver collects a sea bottom mineral sample.

One of the world's largest pieces of machinery —the offshore oil drilling platform "*Ocean Master II.*" From the bottom of its fully extended legs to the top of its derrick, the giant platform measures 593 feet. In this artist's drawing, the towering rig's size is compared with the 42-floor Mobil Oil Building in New York City.

children will die of malnutrition, according to predictions by UNICEF scientists. In the world today at least 100,000,000 children are suffering from the nutritional disease kwashiorkor.

Though advances in agriculture continue to be tremendous, and the prospect of producing synthetic food by chemical magic is bright, we must turn to the sea to meet the staggering need for food quickly enough. If we learn to use the sea's resources, we can overcome the world's protein deficiency. Fishermen are now taking in less than 50,000,000 tons of fish each year. Ocean-ologists have estimated that this is only a tiny fraction of the sea's food potential, which has been calculated to run as high as 100,000,000,000 tons a year! Challenged by this knowledge, national and international organizations are plunging into fisheries research, assigning thousands of scientists to explore ways of swiftly speeding up the sea's food yield.

A drawing board conception of a combined nuclear-powered de-salination and electric power plant. The three nuclear reactors and nine turbo-generators in this plant could produce one billion gallons of fresh water daily as well as enough electricity to maintain a city of 5,000,000 people.

U.S. Navy photographers at work off the Bermuda coast.

New fishing vessels that are really floating factories . . . electronic fish detectors . . . capturing fish with electricity . . . chemical and undersea "vacuum cleaners" . . . creating new kinds of fish . . . new techniques to preserve fish . . . fish flour . . . fish farming . . . sea agriculture to utilize seaweed . . . these are but a few of the new ways in which the edible riches of the sea are being harvested by scientists and engineers. We will find out much more about food from the sea in Chapter 4.

The search for minerals

Prospecting for undersea minerals is so new that scientists have not yet been able to estimate the value of the mineral wealth that lies on and under the sea floor. They do know, however, that it is a vastly greater treasure trove than has been found on and under dry land.

With hundreds of sea-going geologists roving the World Ocean, almost daily reports of new discoveries bring the comforting news that the world is far richer in minerals than many believed. Consider a single mineral, phosphorite, a vital ingredient of fertilizers. The present world production of some 40,000,000 tons a year falls far short of meeting the needs of even present-day agriculture. The sea prospectors report that they have found more of this precious mineral in easily accessible spots off the Continental Shelf than exists in all the known reserves on land.

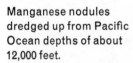

Manganese nodules dredged up from Pacific Ocean depths of about 12,000 feet.

The Westinghouse three-man submersible, "*Deepstar*-4000," is shown here beginning its spiralling descent to the ocean floor. As the vehicle reaches the dark depths, lights are used for studying biological life and ocean conditions and a telescoping motion-picture light is used for photography. The vehicle has a hydraulically controlled claw and specimèn basket for retrieving samples.

Huge deposits of ores containing other much-needed minerals, including aluminum, iron, copper, tin, cobalt and nickel, have been located by prospectors armed with many devices, ranging from underwater television to undersea "workboats" which carry men right down to the sea floor. The deposits they have found already seem almost inexhaustible.

Taking up the search for mineral discoveries under the sea, mining engineers are working right behind the prospecting scientists. Their task is to design the machines that will raise the new-found minerals. Off England, Canada and Japan they have driven coal mines under the sea. In other places, they are trying out adaptations of open-pit mining, employing giant mechanical shovels to lay bare ore beds lying hundreds of feet below the sea floor. And, where prospectors have found great deposits of minerals lying right on the sea floor, the engineers are trying out undersea ore-gathering machines that simply sweep up the treasure. In Chapter 5 are full details.

The challenge of oil

Is there enough petroleum to meet the growing needs of a world that seems to run on oil?

"Plenty," reply the petroleum geologists who, by the hundreds, have gone to sea to find the black gold on which our civilization so depends. On the basis of discoveries already made, they estimate that there are 400,000,000,000 barrels of oil on

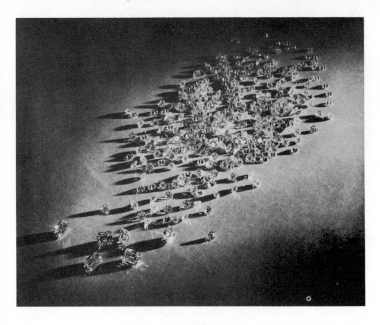

Diamonds are now mined at sea. A vast treasure trove of these precious gems lies under the ocean floor.

A striking example of the powers of undersea cameras. These are the bones of a seal photographed on the ocean floor of the North Pacific. The round object at the right is a current compass which shows the direction of water flow and orients the photograph with respect to magnetic north.

Interior of a huge generator being installed in the world's first large tidal power plant, in the estuary of the River Rance in France.

Sea-going geologists examine rock chips from an underwater drilling site.

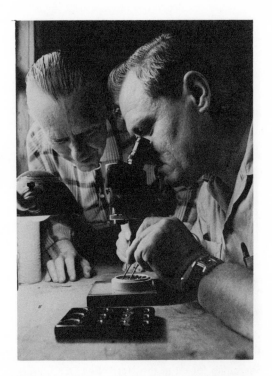

the Continental Shelf alone. They can state confidently that there is more oil at sea depths of less than 1,000 feet than all the known reserves under dry land.

Though the problems of prospecting for underwater oil were great, the mightiest challenge to the oceanologists lies in devising means of getting it out. They are meeting that challenge dramatically with giant platforms, some of which can actually walk into the water; super-powerful drills; underwater robots; submarines with mechanical arms; and human oil-field workers who carry out their activities on the floor of the sea. Chapter 6 gives the whole story.

Converting sea water

In 1950, the U.S. used 200,000,000,000 gallons of water a day. Fifteen years later it

"*Star I*," a one-man research submarine, undergoing tests. The compact vessel can quickly be airlifted to any site where a submarine is needed.

Searching for oil in the North Sea. An underwater explosion is set off and instruments on board the ship record the sound waves which bounce off the layers of subsurface rock. The wave patterns provide clues to the location of oil and gas reservoirs below the sea bottom.

needed 340,000,000,000 gallons daily. By 1980 it will required 600,000,000,000 gallons!

Where will the water come from? There is only one answer: From the sea.

It is big news for a thirsty world that science has already made a dramatic break-through in getting water from the place that contains 97 per cent of the world's supply of this indispensable liquid. Nuclear power has been harnessed to take the salt out of sea water in plants that are going into operation in the U.S. and in many other parts of the world. Soon a mighty flow of fresh water from the sea will turn deserts into gardens and end the menace of water shortage that has plagued the world's great cities.

Along with this boon to mankind, science is going to realize an old dream—that of extracting the mineral riches which sea water contains. Up to now, though it has long been known that sea water contains every element, including gold, science has succeeded in capturing only two of them, bromine and magnesium.

It may take some time, but engineers are certain they can devise ways to extract the mineral riches locked in sea water. We will read much more about this in Chapter 7.

New sea frontiers

The sea presents many other challenges to science beyond those of tapping its abundance of food, minerals and water.

Men have always talked of harnessing the vast energy of the tides. Today this age-old dream is already being realized in some parts of the world, as pioneering tidal power plants go into operation. Chapter 8 tells the story of these engineering triumphs.

Can we learn to predict and control destructive waves and storms spawned at sea? Science is seeking answers to this challenging question. In Chapters 9 and 10 we discuss recent progress in our efforts to tame the sea.

A telemetering buoy which records oceanographic data continuously—even during hurricanes.

The six-man Perry "*Cubmarine*" was one of the many submersibles used in the H-bomb search off the coast of Spain. The "*Cubmarine*" is used for comparatively shallow water research, its extreme diving depth being 600 feet.

U.S. Navy scientists are training dolphins to become assistants to human deep-sea divers.

Scientists at work in university, government and industrial laboratories are exploring what may be the farthest frontier of ocean science—turning man himself into an aquatic creature. A human being equipped with artificial "gills" has already stayed under water for hours without any supply of oxygen other than that extracted from the water itself! In Chapter 10 you will read about this remarkable advance in man's conquest of "Inner Space."

2. MAN IN THE SEA

On the sea floor, 600 feet below the surface, a diver moves slowly along, probing the earth with a pick. After a time, he finds what he wants, drops a specimen into a basket he carries. Then he swims to an underwater structure and emerges into a warm, lighted room where a hot lunch is waiting for him.

* * *

At a depth of 20,000 feet, a saucer-like craft swings into action. Bright lights streaming from it probe the darkness in this sunless deep. Swiftly it moves along the sea floor. Inside, an operator watching a screen tells his companion, "That's the place."

The saucer spins sharply and settles to the floor. A long, hand-like steel appendage reaches out from the craft, scoops up several dozen rocks protruding from the sediment. Deftly the metal arm drops them into a metal container. The submersible darts forward, seeking another ocean treasure.

* * *

Fish swimming in the warm waters of the Gulf Stream suddenly become aware of a strange new visitor to their realm, which moves along, making no sound, and apparently presents no danger to them. The fish finally swim unconcernedly around it. One school of fish comes so close that some of its members actually touch the Plexiglas windows, to the delight of the watching scientists inside. The men are achieving one of their objectives—close-up observation of marine life—in this strange new undersea vehicle, as they float along the Gulf Stream in a 1,500-mile voyage beneath the sea.

Key to ocean riches

These are actual scenes. To tap the riches of the sea, man has learned that he must go *into* the sea. It is not enough to drop even the most sensitive instruments and complicated tools from surface vessels. Remarkable as the floating laboratories that ply the seas may be, the men aboard them cannot accomplish many of the tasks necessary to advance the great ocean venture. Science and engineering have had to find ways to permit men to move freely through the water under the surface, to go down to the ocean floor—however deep it may be—to observe, to study, to measure, to collect mineral and biological samples, and to live and work comfortably in the water.

In the 1960's, science made two spectacular advances. One has been the development of a new breed of submersibles—small, immensely strong craft that can protect men from the awesome pressures while they move through the deepest seas. The other has been to put man directly in the sea without the protective housing of a vehicle, to equip him instead with a suit that will keep him warm, with apparatus to provide him with the breath of life, and with tools he can use to perform underwater tasks.

Submersible capabilities

Unlike naval submarines, which are designed for military purposes, the new submersibles are versatile craft, capable of performing many different tasks. For an at-a-glance indication of their usefulness, look at the list of submersible capabilities outlined by the makers of the *Deepstar* diving saucers.

COMMERCIAL

Assist in deep water petroleum production.
Explore and recover mineral resources.
Survey bottom and inspect underwater pipelines and cables.
Perform salvage operations.
Perform underwater photography.
Become ocean engineering vehicles.
Inspect sites for bottom installations.

The bathyscaph "*Trieste*," designed by Auguste Piccard. In 1960 Piccard's son, Jacques, and U.S. Navy Lieutenant Donald Walsh descended in the "*Trieste*" to the deepest spot in the world's oceans—the bottom of the Marianas Trench, 35,800 feet below sea level.

SCIENTIFIC

Explore bottom and observe geological formations, sediment transport and submarine canyons.

Provide oceanographic instrumentation research.

Observe, research and collect marine life.

Collect deep ocean samples.

Perform medical research—physiological experimentation support.

Make biological, physical, and chemical studies.

Study fish population.

Measure radioactivity in waste disposal.

Make acoustic measurements.

Make geophysical measurements and surveys.

MILITARY

Perform rescue operations.

Use its observation platform for viewing weapon firings.

Perform salvage and weapon recovery operations.

Support underwater instrumentation systems.

Provide bottom-mounted systems.

Aid in mine warfare countermeasures.

Measure machinery noise radiation.

GENERAL

Make environmental testings of materials and components.

Allow underwater sound research.

Support ocean engineering projects.

Provide underwater power plant support.

Exploit food resources from the sea.

Provide underwater inspection and maintenance.

Measure corrosion and marine fouling.

The submersible story

The history of deep-sea submersibles does not go back nearly so far as that of the naval submarines which ply shallower waters. Actually, the idea of penetrating ocean depths in a vehicle took shape in the late 1920's in the mind of the American biologist, William Beebe. For years Beebe, a pioneer diver who used a diving helmet for his investigations off the shores of the U.S. and Caribbean islands, had dreamed of going deeper than any submarine had ever gone.

Though he was not an engineer, he began to work up plans for a deep submersible. It took the shape of a long cylinder that would stand upright. There would be a seat in the middle for a man. Engineers shook their heads when they saw his plans. Such a device simply could not be made strong enough, they told him, to withstand pressures at the half-mile depths Beebe proposed to penetrate.

Among the readers of newspaper stories about Beebe's plans was a young geologist and engineer named Otis Barton. He too had dreamed of a craft that could take a man deep underwater, and he had evolved what he considered a practical design. The strongest possible shape, he had determined, would be a sphere. It would have none of the problems of fabrication present in Beebe's cylinder.

Joining forces, Barton and Beebe, with the help of many engineers, and with the sponsorship of the New York Zoological Society and the National Geographic Society, built a steel sphere. It was large enough to hold two men, and had heavy steel walls, $1\frac{1}{2}$ inches thick,

and 5 viewing windows, each 6 inches in diameter, covered with 3-inch-thick fused quartz glass. For their undersea craft they coined the name *Bathysphere*, meaning "deep sphere."

After 31 trial dives, the *Bathysphere* was winched into the sea off Nonsuch Island, Bermuda, on August 15, 1934. Beebe and Barton were going to try for the bottom, some 3,000 feet down. They dived successfully to this realm never before penetrated by man, and described their reactions via the telephone line that connected them with the mother ship above.

No man ever went so deep again until 1948, when Otis Barton made a descent in the *Benthoscope*, a craft similar to the original *Bathysphere*. This time, off the California coast, he reached a depth of 4,500 feet.

Man had still not succeeded in travelling a mile straight down into the sea, but a daring Belgian scientist, Auguste Piccard, saw no reason why this, and far greater depths, should not be conquered. Piccard had already won world fame by ascending in a balloon of his own design to a record height of 51,775 feet. Now he proposed to put to work in an undersea craft the same principles which had been employed in his stratosphere balloon. With his son, Jacques, and a group of engineers, he designed the *Bathyscaph*, or "deep boat." It was the first deep-diving vehicle with a self-contained electrical and air supply,

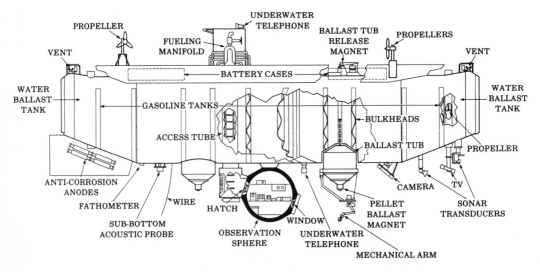

A diagram of the "*Trieste*," first of the modern submersibles.

"*Alvin*," the U.S. Navy's deep-diving research submarine. In the 22-foot vehicle, oceanographers can carry out scientific studies at depths up to 6,000 feet. Its large main propeller at the stern can be turned from side to side to steer the vehicle, enabling "*Alvin*" to make a complete 360-degree turn with a radius of less than its own length.

which left it free of any physical connection with a mother ship. Named the FRNS-3 after its purchase by the French Navy, the craft slid down through the waters of the Atlantic off French West Africa. Past Barton's record depth of 4,500 feet it went . . . past the one-mile mark . . . past two miles. It stopped its descent at 13,284 feet.

Undersea balloon

Some said that this record would stand for a long time. The Piccards disagreed. They were already at work on the *Trieste*, a remarkable craft which was to embody many improvements.

The *Trieste* has been called an "undersea balloon" because it is made up of the same two assemblies used in balloons designed to float in the air—a buoyancy chamber and a cabin. Just as the balloon bag is filled with lighter-than-air gas, so the float of a bathycaph is filled with lighter-than-water liquid. Like a balloon, the underwater craft is designed to go up and down by weight control. In the case of the aerial balloon this is accomplished by dropping ballast, or valving off some of the gas. In the case of the *Trieste* it is accomplished by discharging steel ballast or by valving off fluid to make the craft lighter or heavier than the surrounding water.

After watching early tests of the *Trieste*, the U.S. Navy expressed an interest in buying the craft, which it subsequently did.

Asked how deep the *Trieste* would go, Jacques Piccard gave a direct answer. "To the bottom," he said, "wherever the bottom is."

In its surface position, "*Alvin*" looks more like a bathtub toy than a research vessel. Here the two-man sub is readied for a dive in search of the lost H-bomb off Palomares, Spain.

Project Nekton

Assignment: Descend to the deepest part of the World Ocean.

That was the task handed Jacques Piccard and Lieutenant Don Walsh in the U.S. Navy's Project Nekton.

The bottom was far, far below them when the two crawled into the entrance shaft of the *Trieste* on January 23, 1960, a date boldly circled on the calendar of great events in the history of man's exploration of the deep sea. For two days the U.S.S. *Lewis* had been dropping TNT—160,000 pounds of it—overside in an effort to find the very deepest part of the Pacific Ocean's Marianas Trench, which had long been established as the deepest spot in all the World Ocean. Dr. Andreas Reichnitzer, director of the project, was personally timing the interval between an explosion on the sea floor and the snapping noise the returning sound waves made in a headset he wore. At last he found what he wanted—a spot where the sound took 14 seconds to reach the surface. That depth must be 33,000 feet. Here was the place for the *Trieste* to go down.

The submersible worked as well in this deepest dive as it had in the 70 lesser ones it had already made. Silently it dropped through the water . . . down past the 24,000-foot level that Piccard and Walsh had reached a few weeks before . . . down past 30,000. And then, amazingly, past the 33,000 feet where Reichnitzer had calculated the bottom lay.

Piccard and Walsh stared at each other in puzzlement. The *Trieste* was at 34,000 feet; still no bottom. Then 35,000 feet. Still the echo sounder was finding no floor from which to bounce back its sound waves. Finally, at 35,500, there it was . . . a clear indication that the bottom was still 300 feet below.

Slowly the *Trieste* dropped downwards. Now the searchlight's rays were reflected from the ghostly grey of the floor. At 1:06 in the afternoon, 4 hours and 38 minutes after they started, the submersible settled gently into the sediment—35,800 feet down!

Though the *Trieste*'s descent had no immediate practical value, it was rated a spectacular scientific success. It proved once and for all that any who doubted the ability of a submersible to go to the greatest depths were wrong. It proved, too, that a manned submersible can bring back priceless information that is difficult, or impossible, to gather with devices operated from the surface. For the voyagers into the deep found a decisive answer to a question that had always tantalized oceanographers. Are there living creatures in the eternally dark parts of the sea?

When Piccard and Walsh peered out of the porthole as the *Trieste* lay on the floor of the Marianas Trench, they saw a fish—a brown, flat-bodied creature about a foot long. It was not very big to be sure, but it was a fish, and it was swimming about unconcernedly at a depth where scientists had once thought no life could exist.

Search for the Thresher

The *Trieste* dramatically proved its undersea powers when the U.S. nuclear submarine *Thresher* sank on April 10, 1963. With the lost submarine somewhere on the floor of the sea, more than 8,000 feet down, the U.S. Navy realized that the only undersea craft it had which could search for the remains of the *Thresher* was the deep-sea submersible *Trieste*.

The craft was called away from its research work in the Pacific and sent to the Atlantic.

It soon proved its value, and, in so doing, opened a new era in undersea research. The submersible's first descent at the scene was a failure, since the two observers aboard saw only the drab sea floor. On the second dive, the men had a narrow escape. When a large object showed on the sonar gear, the pilot, Lieutenant George Martin, was so intent on studying it that he steered the submersible into the mud, where she stuck fast. For more than half an hour he and his companion, Kenneth MacKenzie, tried to rock the craft loose. Were they going to be trapped here in the depths? At last, with a jerk, the *Trieste* broke free and shot upwards.

This experience did not keep the men from making a third dive, which brought results. Through the observation window they caught sight of something yellow. Moving the submersible closer, they could see that it was a plastic shoe cover of the type worn by men who worked in the reactor compartment of a nuclear submarine. The men aboard the submersible were able to read the letters on it—"SSN-5"—the U.S. Navy's designating label on equipment aboard nuclear submarines.

Encouraged by this find, the *Trieste* made a number of other dives, many of them fruitless. However, on August 29, the men peering through the window saw something that brought a cry to their lips. Twisted pipes . . . a torn cable . . . ragged pieces of metal. They lay scattered over a wide area. They had

Major General D. E. Wilson and Admiral W. S. Guest, heads of the U.S. Air Force and U.S. Navy search operations at Palomares, Spain, inspect the H-bomb which had been lost in the sea for nearly three months. The equipment in the background is the recovery vehicle CURV which attached the raising lines to the bomb.

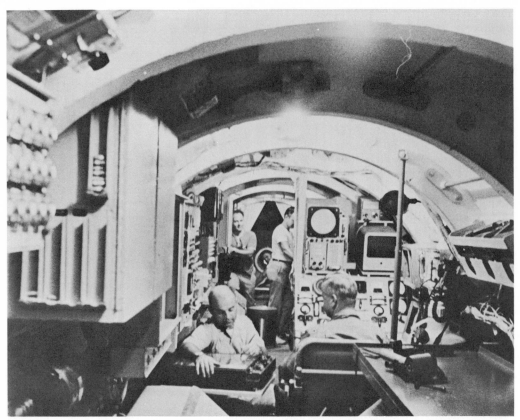

Members of the "*Aluminaut's*" crew go about their duties. The interior of the 51-foot vessel is crammed with 3 tons of scientific equipment.

found the *Thresher*. It was a triumph for the *Trieste*, and dramatic proof that the deep-sea submersible could explore minutely an area of sea floor as nothing else could do.

The new submersibles

A whole fleet of submersibles was launched in the 1960's. Included was a new kind of undersea craft—a small, specialized "workboat," designed to accomplish particular aquatic tasks. Some workboats are equipped for fisheries research, others for deep-sea mineral prospecting, still others for salvage, and so on down a long list.

Though other craft exist on the drawing boards, the submersibles here described are the major ones already in use.

Trieste II

A modified form of the history-making *Trieste I*, this new submersible cannot dive as deep as the original, but it has new capabilities

that make it a more versatile craft for undersea research.

Its photographic system alone is a marvel that turns the *Trieste II* into a giant moving camera. Outside are three cameras synchronized with strobe lights. Pictures are taken every 4 seconds, covering a bottom area 6 by 21 feet. Inside the craft is another camera, which peers out through a window and can be synchronized with the external cameras. With all four cameras concentrating on a small section of the sea floor, extremely accurate and detailed pictures can be obtained, giving a multi-dimensional view of any object.

Equally advanced is the ship's sonar mapping system. This sensitive new system can detect, and indicate on screens, even tiny objects ahead of the submersible, or it can be adjusted to "describe" a wide area far ahead.

Automatic instruments continually monitor a variety of conditions, including depth, water temperature, sound speed, water noise, and salinity of the water. A device which measures current speed when the *Trieste II* is at rest on the bottom is so sensitive that it can detect a speed as low as .03 of a knot.

In addition, other equipment can be put aboard for specialized voyages of exploration. Plankton samplers, sediment sounders, velocity probes, and core samplers are some of the devices added to the sub's regular equipment.

A powerful mechanical arm mounted in the stern gives scientists the ability to pick up and carry to the surface objects weighing as much as 500 pounds. A television camera located in the arm gives the operator the visibility he would have if he were just inches away from the specimen he is grasping with his mighty metal hand.

Alvin

This easily controlled little craft played a leading rôle in locating the lost H bomb which fell into the water off the coast of Spain in 1965. Named after Alvin C. Vine, Woods Hole Oceanographer, *Alvin*, which was built for the U.S. Navy by Litton Industries, is one of the new breed of work submersibles which can perform a variety of undersea tasks.

Its large main propeller at the stern can be turned from side to side to steer the vehicle in the same manner as an outboard motor boat. A complete 360-degree turn with a radius less than the length of the boat itself can be made in about 45 seconds. On each side, just to the rear of the 5-foot conning tower, is a small lift propeller which can be rotated so as to direct its thrust up or down, ahead or astern. All three propellers are controlled by an aircraft-type control stick inside the sphere.

A unique variable ballast system compensates for the weight of personnel and instruments, and for changes in the density of sea water. This system consists of pressure-proof aluminum spheres interconnected with collapsible rubber bags partially filled with oil. In order to increase buoyancy the bags are expanded by oil pumped from the spheres into the bags, increasing the displacement of sea water without adding to the weight of the vehicle. The oil can be pumped from the bags back into the spheres to make the vessel heavier. The system permits adjustments of plus or minus 600 pounds.

Four viewing ports permit observations ahead of and beneath the vehicle. Additional monitoring is provided by a scanning sonar set and a closed circuit television system. An up-and-down echo sounder also gives both height above the bottom and depth below the surface. Constant voice and code communication with the surface is maintained by a sonar telephone system. Regular equipment for oceanographic studies includes an under-

Commander M. Scott Carpenter, U.S. Navy, the astronaut who took to the sea, checks an electrically heated wet suit prior to an underwater test.

water camera with associated lights and a mechanical arm for picking up objects on the ocean bottom.

The mother vessel for *Alvin* is a specially designed catamaran barge supported by two floats, each 96 feet long and displacing approximately 400 tons. The barge has a platform which can be raised to lift *Alvin* from the water. Mounted on the barge are four portable vans for servicing the vehicle. Although the catamaran has to be towed by a tug over long distances, it has self-propulsion for daily short-range operations.

A number of safety features have been built into *Alvin* to return the occupants to the surface in case of accident or malfunction. The three batteries can be dropped to reduce the weight of the vehicle, and the mechanical arm can be detached if it should become hopelessly entangled or if additional buoyancy is needed. As a last resort, the pressure sphere itself can be disconnected and will rise to the surface with the crew aboard, since it is positively buoyant. In shallow water the occupants can escape from the sphere by means of scuba gear stored in the vehicle. Chemical fire extinguishers are also carried.

Aluminaut

The *Aluminaut* is the first submarine to be built entirely of aluminum. Fifty feet long, it is made of 11 large aluminum cylinders so carefully machined that, without the use of gaskets, they could be bolted together to make a watertight, cylindrical hull. This makes a sturdy structure that can withstand a pressure of 60,000 pounds per square inch, giving an ample margin of safety at 15,000 feet. This three-man submersible, made by the Electric Boat Company, a division of General Dynamics, carries a pilot and two scientists, and is

A drawing of "*Autec I*," a research and work submarine with two mechanical arms which make it able to perform complex tasks.

24

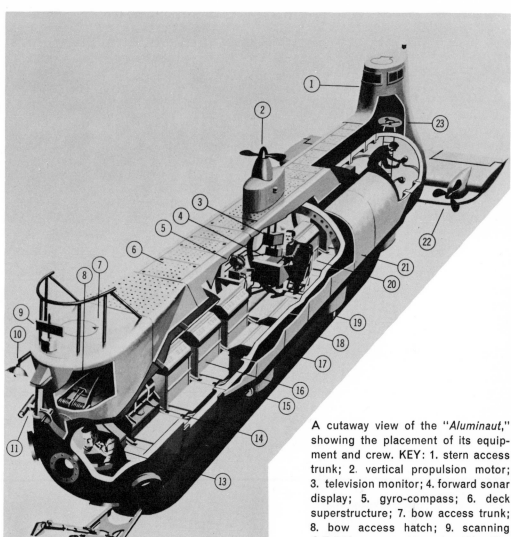

A cutaway view of the "*Aluminaut*," showing the placement of its equipment and crew. KEY: 1. stern access trunk; 2. vertical propulsion motor; 3. television monitor; 4. forward sonar display; 5. gyro-compass; 6. deck superstructure; 7. bow access trunk; 8. bow access hatch; 9. scanning C.T.F.M. sonar; 10. extensible illuminator; 11. television camera and illuminator; 12. manipulator device; 13. observer; 14. oxygen flask; 15. port illuminator; 16. battery; 17. side-looking sonar (under ballast tank); 18. keel superstructure; 19. shot ballast solenoid; 20. skipper; 21. ballast tank; 22. port propulsion motor; 23. stern access hatch.

powered by storage batteries which enable it to cruise submerged for 72 hours.

The Deepstar diving saucers

The *Deepstars* are a family of undersea workboats, designed for work at different depths. They include *Deepstar-4,000, Deepstar-12,000* and *Deepstar-20,000*. Descendants of the diving saucers developed in France, they are being built by the Underseas Division of the Westinghouse Company, working with the French Office of Undersea Research.

Deepstar-4000, which can serve as an example of the deeper diving saucers, was constructed in a unique manner. First two hemispheres of alloy steel were welded together. After testing, 11 holes were made in the craft—the hatch opening, 2 viewing ports, 2 electric cable passages, 5 small shaft

Like two friendly porpoises, "*Star II*" and " *Star III*" go through sea trials at Groton, Connecticut.

openings, and a camera port. Observation from *Deepstar-4000* is made from 2 large Plexiglas windows in the forward lower part of the sphere. These windows give an overlapping horizontal view of approximately 150 degrees to the observer and pilot, who lie prone on couches. A tilting seat near the middle of the sphere accommodates the co-pilot or second observer.

A mercury system controls the pitch of the vehicle. Two large pistons in fore and aft tanks pump mercury back and forth, shifting the vehicle's center of gravity rapidly. This tilts the craft upwards or downwards.

Located outside the *Deepstar* are accessories that enable it to carry out a variety of useful activities. They include a lamp-carrying arm with hydraulic remote control for use with

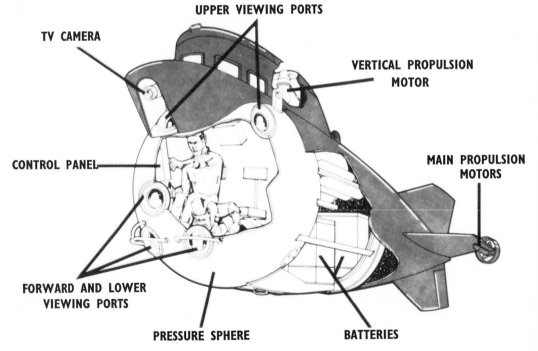

A cutaway view of the 17-foot submarine "*Star II*."

The aluminum outer hull of "*Deep Quest.*"

motion picture camera, strobe flash and camera mounts, a mechanical arm with sample-collecting tongs, a sample basket and a running light.

The *Deepstars* are not kept in the water when finished with their work, but are hoisted aboard a mother ship, where a 20-by-30-foot area on the ship's deck serves as the vehicle's parking space.

Deep Quest

Though it is only 40 feet long, *Deep Quest* can accommodate four persons and carry 7,000 pounds of machinery and equipment. This submersible, launched in 1967, is described by her builders, Lockheed Missile and Spacecraft Corp., as a "versatile multi-mission research craft, capable of carrying out a variety of missions in the testing of components and materials needed for exploration and exploitation of the virtually untapped riches of the sea."

Though it can descend to 6,000 feet, *Deep Quest* finds its greatest use at the lesser depths of the Continental Shelf, where it is a major

The submarine "*Deep Quest*'s" gleaming steel inner hull during construction.

A hydrodynamics research specialist tests a scale model of "*Deep Quest.*"

tool of prospecting for undersea mineral deposits.

PLC-4

The neat little Perry-Link Submersible is designed as a working craft. Only 22 feet long and 9 feet high, it has been likened to a helicopter in its performance. Actuated by aircraft-type controls, it can be "flown" forwards or backwards, or can hover perfectly still in all but swift currents. It is designed as a two-man craft. The pilot sits with his head in the conning tower, where he has 360-degree vision through portholes. The co-pilot may sit or lie down.

PX-15

The *PX-15*, designed by Jacques Piccard and built by Grumman Aircraft Engineering Corp., is unique in its ability to float at a constant depth without expending energy or making noise. This makes it an ideal submersible for certain special research projects, such as recording sounds made by sea creatures, and observing fish and sea mammals which are attracted to the silent, floating craft.

The *PX-15*'s first major assignment, after its launching in 1967, was a 1,500-mile undersea float from Florida to Nova Scotia, permitting observations inside the Gulf Stream never made before. Larger than most research submersibles, the *PX-15* carries a crew of five and is equipped with a laboratory and living quarters, including galley, showers, bunks, etc.

Scuba, an undersea tool

For well over a century men have been able to work in the water in limited ways, in diving suit and helmet, connected by an air hose to a ship above. But not until the coming of scuba (for *S*elf-*C*ontained *U*nderwater *B*reathing *A*pparatus) did men achieve complete mobility undersea.

Actually, the idea of underwater breathing apparatus is not new. Men had been experimenting with it for half a century when, in 1943, Jacques-Yves Cousteau, the famous French diver, developed the aqualung as we know it today. The key to his apparatus, which has made scuba diving possible, is an automatic regulator which feeds the proper amount of air from a tank carried on his back to the diver regardless of his position.

Scuba diving, besides being an engrossing pastime for hundreds of thousands—and soon, many believe, for millions—is a key to the underwater riches of the Continental Shelf. Geologists, marine biologists, and oceanographers in all specialties have turned to scuba to give them a first-hand view of the undersea world. Scuba-diving prospectors seek out undersea mineral finds. Petroleum companies employ scuba-equipped divers to cap and repair undersea oil wells. Scuba divers work on many undersea salvage operations.

Versatile and useful as scuba is, one serious drawback has been limiting its application. In its original and familiar form it was not suited for deep dives. However, thanks to a young college student inventor, millions of square miles of sea floor are no longer off limits for scuba divers.

Scuba for deep dives

Alan Krasberg became interested in skin diving while a high school student. However, diving 75 and 100 feet with an aqualung was not enough for him. He was fascinated by the dark depths of the sea, and wanted to go deeper than man had ever gone before—or make it possible for other men to do so.

By 1960, Krasberg was a graduate student at Harvard. Though his subject was astrophysics, his diving hobby was his major interest: he wanted to develop a means to swim and explore the seas at depths of 1,000, 1,500, or even 2,000 feet.

"Impossible," the experts said.

The barrier to truly deep dives was oxygen poisoning. As a diver goes down, his diving apparatus automatically allows the pressure of the "air" or gas mixture he breathes to increase. Since the pressure increases by 1 atmosphere (the pressure at sea level) for each 33 feet of descent, this means that a diver at 100 feet is breathing air at 3 times surface pressure. Since the air thus compressed contains 3 times as many molecules, the diver is breathing 3 times as much oxygen as usual. After breathing this oxygen-rich mixture for a time, he is subject to oxygen poisoning, with its symptoms of dizziness, nausea and convulsions. Sometimes the result is death.

What was needed to solve this problem, Krasberg saw, was a device that would measure and control the amount of oxygen in the intake air, whatever the pressure. His solution, discovered after hundreds of experiments, was a tiny electronic mechanism that could sense the number of oxygen molecules in any gas to which it was exposed. Exposure to oxygen has the effect of stepping up the voltage of an electric current. The more oxygen, the higher the voltage. Krasberg hooked his sensor current to a control circuit. As the oxygen level rose, the greater voltage fed into the circuit would cause a valve to close; as the oxygen level fell, the drop in voltage would cause the valve to open.

After testing his device in a crude but workable home-made scuba diving lung, Krasberg knew he had succeeded. He had a machine that could transform deep-sea diving. Now all he had to do was find a company to help him carry out the great amount of development work needed. He found one, a small firm in Cambridge, Massachusetts,

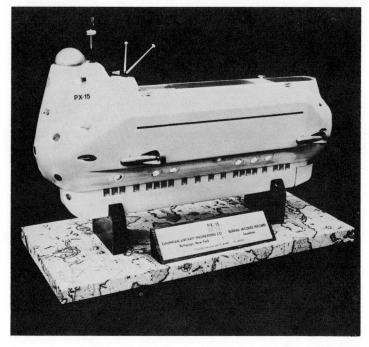

A model of the PX-15, a submersible designed by Jacques Piccard to make long "drift" voyages in major ocean currents, such as the Gulf Stream.

"Soucoupe," Jacques-Yves Cousteau's diving saucer, which pioneered this design for sub-mersibles.

which would back him. A more sophisticated model was made and demonstrated to astonished U.S. Navy officials.

Had a college student, and a small company, operating without government research funds, really solved the problem that had defeated so many other researchers? The answer was a resounding affirmative. The Krasberg lung had indeed done away with the problem of oxygen poisoning. The Navy ordered additional experimental models, and ocean science hailed a new break-through in its effort to conquer the depths.

Because of the way it works, the Krasberg Lung has other important advantages besides its basic ability to prevent oxygen poisoning. One of the drawbacks of ordinary scuba gear is its wastefulness of air. At the surface, your lungs use only 4 per cent of the air you breathe in. The other 96 per cent is expelled. Underwater, a scuba diver breathing compressed air actually uses an even smaller percentage. Because the air is compressed, he takes in more at a single breath—13 times as much air at a 400-foot pressure, for example—yet his lungs use only the same amount they would on the surface. The result is that a tank of compressed air lasts only a limited time—the lower the depth and the greater the pressure, the shorter the time—because with each gulp the diver breathes out so much air.

The obvious answer is a "closed system," one in which the waste breathing gas or air is not wasted in the water, but is kept in the breathing system and recirculated, after the carbon dioxide is chemically removed. The U.S. Navy has had such a closed system apparatus for many years, but its use was limited to shallow water. Without some way to control the amount of oxygen, its use in deep water—that is, under higher pressures —would be deadly. Krasberg's control solves this problem and permits the use of the closed system at great depths and pressures. The closed system apparatus, as finally developed, uses three tanks, one of helium, one of oxygen, and a third of the chemical that "scrubs" the helium-oxygen mixture after breathing. A single foot-long tank of oxygen now lasts a diver 6 hours at any depth, permitting a far longer underwater stay than ever before without tank replacement.

"*Starfish House*," Captain Cousteau's undersea dwelling. In it, men can live under the sea for weeks at a time.

Undersea chambers

Three great pioneers have contributed to the development of another important tool that aids exploitation of undersea riches. They are Jacques-Yves Cousteau, Captain George Bond of the U.S. Navy, and Edwin A. Link, inventor of the Link trainer, which has taught thousands of aviators. Each of these three had a vision of a type of equipment that would play a rôle in the conquest of the seas. What was needed, they believed, was some kind of undersea chamber, a home in the water, which could serve as a base for working divers.

Cousteau's approach was to create Starfish House, a structure in which, in 1962, he and two of his men spent a week under 40 feet of water in what was called Continental Shelf Expedition No. 1. Later, in Conshelf No. 2, eight men stayed under the Red Sea for a month. During their stay they performed numerous tasks and went through many tests. They even had a "garage" in which they kept an undersea vehicle, a diving saucer designed by Cousteau.

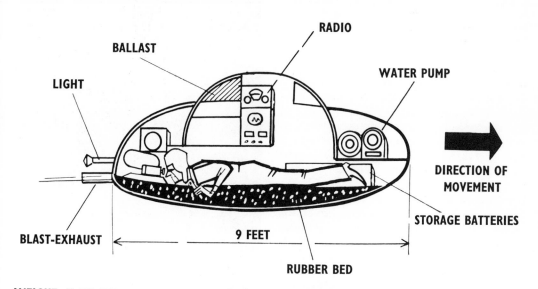

RADIO

BALLAST

LIGHT

WATER PUMP

DIRECTION OF MOVEMENT

STORAGE BATTERIES

BLAST-EXHAUST

9 FEET

RUBBER BED

WEIGHT: 7,600 LBS.   SPEED: 65 FT. PER MIN.   DEPTH: 1,637 FT.

A diagram of Cousteau's underwater saucer.

U.S. Navy underseas habitat "*Sealab II*," which housed the Navy's aquanauts at a depth of 210 feet for extended periods.

Bond began his pioneering work with Project Genesis. In a series of tests at the Naval Medical Research Laboratory in New London, Connecticut, divers lived on the surface for long periods under pressures that would be required at various depths. In a final experiment, three men "stayed down" for 12 days at a pressure simulating the pressure existing 200 feet down.

After this initial experiment, Bond directed Project Sealab, in which a 10-ton cigar-shaped dwelling was lowered into the sea off Bermuda. In it four aquanauts lived for 12 days, swimming out of the chamber to perform work, and carrying out many experiments breathing different mixtures of helium and oxygen. An outgrowth of this project is Sealab III, of 1967, involving a much larger chamber, more men, and a variety of undersea experiments.

Edwin Link's project was named Man-in-Sea. For it, Link designed several important pieces of apparatus. One was the Link Cylinder, a pressurized chamber in which divers could be lowered into, and raised from, the sea. Another part of the Man-in-Sea apparatus was a remarkable inflatable undersea house called SPID (for Submersible Portable Inflatable Dwelling). Link felt that

The SPID—an underwater habitat used in the 1964 Link dives in the Bahamas, where Jon Lindbergh and Robert Stenuit spent 49 hours at a depth of 432 feet.

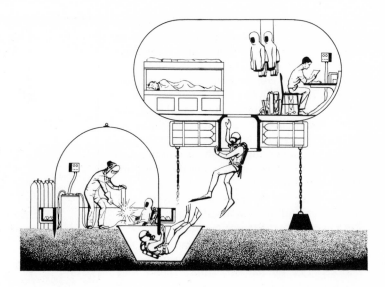

SPID adapted for use as an underwater habitat for working divers.

it was a considerable advance over the rigid structures of Sealab and Conshelf.

"The inflatable type of dwelling . . . is easier to handle and more economical," he stated. "It can be carried on a smaller ship and is less hazardous to put on the bottom as it does not have to be inflated until it is in position. Also, it is less likely to fatigue and crack than metal, which is permanently stretched with each exposure to pressure."

Divers Robert Stenuit and Jon Lindbergh lived in SPID in complete comfort, eating, sleeping and resting between stretches of exploring and working on the sea floor. Though their stay was only 49 hours in a first project, this trial run proved the practicability of setting up undersea bases anywhere on the Continental Shelf.

Cachalot

A diving system developed by Westinghouse enables divers to live as well as work undersea for a week at a time, continuously breathing a helium-oxygen-nitrogen mixture, and never going through decompression. Called *Cachalot*, after the deep-diving sperm whale, the apparatus consists of a submersible pressure chamber, a deck pressure chamber, and all the associated equipment needed to keep a crew of eight divers at work.

The process starts when the divers enter the submersible chamber. In it the pressure is built up to that of the level at which they plan to work. At a 200-foot working depth, this pressure would be about 100 pounds per square inch. Once on the sea floor, the divers drop through a hatch into the water. (Pressure in the chamber keeps the water from entering.)

On the ocean floor, they are supplied with the gas mixture by a unit called the Hookah scuba lung, connected by 50-foot hoses to cylinders of oxygen-helium attached to the submersible chamber. The diver wears a full face mask for protection, and under it a nose and mouth mask for breathing. Breathing bags, one for inhalation and one for exhalation, are worn on his chest. The pressure and mixture of the breathing gas are continuously monitored by a Krasberg oxygen sensor. If the amount of oxygen in the diver's gas mixture varies beyond certain limits, the unit warns surface support personnel electronically, by telephone lines connected with the diver, and the diver is ordered back into the submersible chamber.

From time to time, the divers return to the chamber for food and rest. When they all report to the chamber after completion of a day's work, its hatch is closed and the chamber is hoisted to the deck of the mother ship, coming to rest on its pad near the deck chamber. A hydraulic mechanism brings the two chambers together. When an airtight seal is made between them, the divers are free to walk out of the submersible chamber into

33

the more spacious quarters of the deck chamber, in which the gas mixture is kept at exactly the pressure at which they have been working undersea. The deck chamber is equipped with comfortable beds, a reading room, galley, showers, and all requisites.

The next morning, after breakfast, the divers again enter the submersible chamber, which is then sealed and lowered into the sea. They need not go through the decompression process until a week-end, when they customarily take time off.

What are the benefits from this idea of staying beneath the sea until the job is done? Let Diver Robert Stenuit explain:

"An ordinary diver who works for one hour in the open sea, 200 feet down, half knocked out by narcosis, must spend four hours more waiting at different decompression stages before getting back to the surface. One hour of productive effort, therefore, will cost the company employing him a full day's work, while the diver, crew, boat, compressors, and special equipment are immobilized.

"For example, if the job requires 40 hours' effective work at the bottom, it will cost the company 40 full days' work, or two whole months (not counting storms, engine trouble, fog, etc.). If the diver is replaced by a worker living on the bottom around the clock, in some kind of dwelling like a Link cylinder, or submerged house, our man will then work his 8 hours, 5 days at a stretch. He will go home to his comfortable and well-heated shelter for lunch, and to relax and to sleep at night. When the job is done, he will lock himself in his cylinder, and be brought back on board for safe deck decompression in comfort and under medical supervision. His decompression will take 48 hours, but won't immobilize the whole crew of the ship.

"To get the same job completed, done better by a clear-headed diver, who will have taken fewer risks to his life and health, the company will have devoted 5 instead of 60 days, a saving of 12 to 1.

"Besides this particular case, which is typical of any ordinary underwater job such as salvaging wrecks, sewer laying or construction, most of tomorrow's lobster raising, fish farming, mineral extraction, scientific work, etc., will probably require permanent

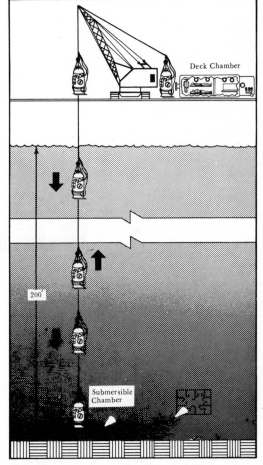

This diagram shows the "Cachalot" deep-sea diving system in operation. Divers remain under deep-sea pressure in the deck chamber after completing a day's work in the sea.

surveillance of the bottom by oceanauts. The ability to live under pressure for weeks and months will be a *sine qua non* condition."

Stenuit and Lindbergh have put the knowledge and experience won in the Man-in-Sea project to work in an extremely practical way. As members of a group known as Offshore Divers, Inc., operating from a base in Santa Barbara, California, they have undertaken tasks of all the types described by Stenuit. Using apparatus based on the design of the Man-in-Sea equipment, they have proved their ability to take mineral samples, fit out undersea oil wells, and perform many complicated underwater tasks at depths as great as 600 feet.

3. SEEING INTO THE SEA

On the screen in front of them scientists aboard a ship prowling the Gulf of Mexico saw, clearly outlined, the crumpled structure of an oil-drilling platform lying on the sea floor. Weeks before it had been swept away in a hurricane.

It would have been remarkable enough if so clear a "picture" had emerged from cameras deep in the sunless sea, but no camera was providing this view of the depths. It was, instead, being brought to the scientists by a new form of sonar. They were seeing with sound.

In their efforts to tap the riches of the sea, oceanologists are employing a host of new and improved instruments, of which sonar is only one. Whatever resource they seek to utilize, the primary objective is to "see" beneath the sea. The apparatus for obtaining ocean data takes many forms. Cameras are suspended from ships or borne through the sea on moving sleds or other platforms; delicate instruments tell how fast an invisible current in the sea is flowing; devices bring up specimens—sea creatures, sea plants, sediment, and soil from the ocean bottom.

Although oceanographers have had some of these instruments for a long time, many have been transformed by modern technology. Still others are completely new, their existence made possible only by recent developments in electronics.

Seeing with sound

One of the key tools of ocean science is echo sounding. Modern echo-sounding instruments, no matter how elaborate, are all based on the same principle. All call for sending out vibrations and picking up echoes on their return, mainly from striking a solid object—the sea floor, fish, a ship, etc.

This calls for three basic parts in the sounding apparatus—a transmitter to send out ultrasonic vibrations; a receiver to pick up and amplify the returning signal; a recording device to indicate and make visual the information provided by the returning signal.

The transmitter produces ultrasonic impulses by various methods. One is through the use of a "sparker," a device which produces an electric spark discharge. Another uses a piezo-electric crystal which expands and contracts, and, in so doing, produces vibrations as an alternating current is applied to it. A third uses the phenomenon of *magneto-constriction*, in which vibrations are produced by the contraction and expansion of nickel plates, brought about by increasing and decreasing a magnetic field in which the plates are located.

These means of producing ultra-sound may be built into a transducer, a device which both transmits and receives. The fact that modern electronic engineers have been able to combine the two eliminates the need for hydrophones, otherwise used to pick up the returning signal. In many types of equipment the hydrophones are towed at a given depth to avoid the possibility of their picking up ship noises which might affect accuracy.

In many devices the recorder consists of a stylus which moves over a sheet of paper marked off in units of measurement. Each time a return signal—an echo—is received, the stylus moves a distance proportional to the time the echo has taken to reach the receiver. Of course, the stylus moves only a minute distance in response to each impulse, but as the impulses come racing in, one after the other, they graphically portray a picture of the sea floor.

Some types of echo-sounding devices replace or supplement the stylus and paper with a cathode-ray tube. The returning

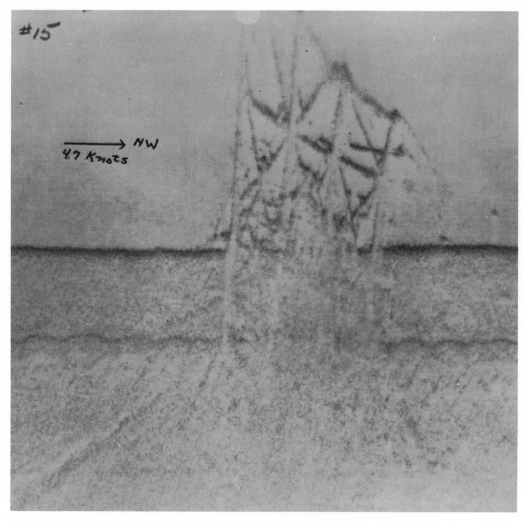

An underwater sonic picture of a sunken oil rig resting on the sea floor.

sound impulses are converted to electrons which, projected by an electron gun at the base of the tube, produce bright lines on the face of the tube. Watchers aboard a ship thus get a continuing picture in multi-line (much like a television picture) of the solid objects from which the ultrasonic waves are echoing.

Through the use of powerful sources of sound that penetrate through sediment and rocks, it is possible to get sound-pictures from considerable depths below the sea floor. This enables scientists to learn much about the structure and nature of earth layers under the water. Penetrations of 1,000 feet under the sea bottom are not uncommon. Knowledge of undersea earth formations is of vital im-

portance to searchers for undersea mineral and oil deposits.

New electronic transducers that deliver sound with pin-point accuracy make echo-sounding a valuable tool for marine biologists. The ultrasonic waves bounce off fish, revealing their depths and speed. Fisheries researchers, following the pioneer efforts of Dr. W. C. Hodgson, Lowestoft Laboratories, British Ministry of Agriculture, Fisheries and Food, have even learned to identify particular kinds of fish by the type of echo they send back.

Seismic waves from earthquakes have revealed much information about the earth's structure. By the speed and nature of the

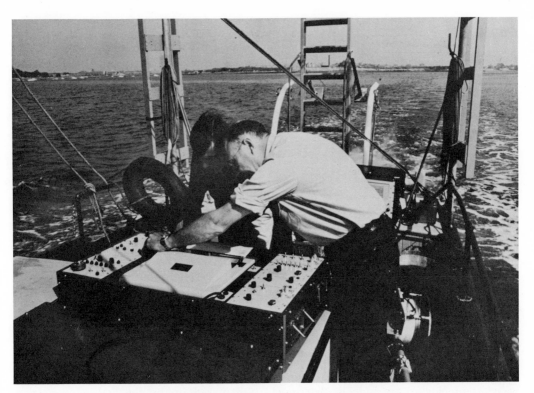

Scientists taking a seismic profile of sub-bottom strata.

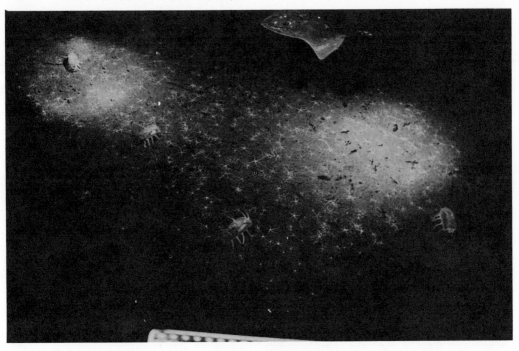

Underwater cameras reveal sea floor details with brilliant clarity. The large creature (above) is a skate. The small pig-like animals are sea cucumbers. On the ocean floor are spiny star fish.

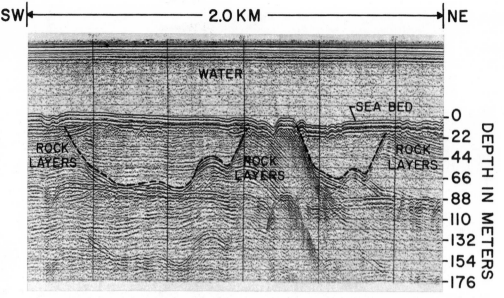

SW |← ———————————— 2.0 KM ———————————— →| NE

WATER

SEA BED

ROCK LAYERS

ROCK LAYERS

ROCK LAYERS

DEPTH IN METERS
- 0
- 22
- 44
- 66
- 88
- 110
- 132
- 154
- 176

A seismic sounding record of the English Channel, made in connection with selection of a route for the proposed Channel Tunnel.

waves, seismologists are able to determine many facts about the rocks the seismic waves have passed through. Miniature, man-made earthquakes are giving sea scientists vital information about the land under the sea— the land in which they seek oil and minerals.

Seismic sounding

In what is called seismic reflection shooting, small explosions of dynamite or TNT dropped into the water produce vibrations that penetrate deeply into sub-sea strata. Some of the vibrations are reflected toward the surface from sediment layers or rocks of different composition. Picked up by hydrophones, these reflected waves are conveyed, as electronic impulses, to recorders on the ship.

In seismic refraction shooting, two vessels are used. One drops the charge as it moves along a planned course. The charge may vary from as little as a half-pound of TNT to as much as 300 pounds. The quantity of explosives is determined by the depth the geologists wish them to penetrate. Large charges can reach down miles into the earth, penetrating through the crust into the upper mantle. Refracted by differences in the densities of materials they strike, the waves

are picked up by the hydrophones of the receiving vessel, which is stationary, its engines off, to avoid any interference with the extremely small vibrations from the earth beneath the sea.

For probing the sea floor under shallow water, apparatus for continuous seismic profiling has been developed. In this case, a towed device sets off a series of gas explosions as the ship moves through the water. Another means of creating sound is with a device that emits a series of powerful electrical discharges which set up sound vibrations.

Undersea photography

Important as sound may be in probing the sea, undersea photography ranks along with it as a means of searching for ocean riches and knowledge. Many important developments have made the underwater camera a versatile instrument that can be used for tasks which, a few years ago, seemed impossible.

The first undersea photographs were made in 1893 by Louis Boutan, a Frenchman who took some remarkable pictures in the shallow waters of the Mediterranean. Published in book form as *La Photographie Sousmarine*, in 1900, they revealed to the world many fascinating glimpses of ocean life. The first undersea color pictures were made many years later, in 1926, by the American biologist, Dr. Samuel J. Longley, working with Charles Martin of the National Geographic Society. Between these milestones, many other efforts were made to use the camera as a tool for ocean research.

Actually, underwater photography as used by today's sea scientists dates only from 1940, when an automatic underwater camera was produced by scientists at Woods Hole Oceanographic Institution in Massachusetts. Suspended by cable from a ship, it took pictures of the ocean bottom at considerable depths. All earlier photographs had been taken at shallow depths with cameras held by divers.

Finding a suitable camera for undersea work has never been much of a problem. Protecting ordinary cameras with waterproof housings presents no great technical difficulties. The major obstacle, and one that took years to overcome, is lighting. In the black depths of the deep sea, never penetrated by sunlight, artificial lights have to be used to obtain pictures, even with the most sensitive film. The problem is not one of simply providing enough light, however. Light passing through water loses some of its intensity through absorption, but, more important, it is also "scattered." This pro-

A hydrophone—an underwater "mike"—is lowered into the sea by an oceanographer.

duces a haze effect on films, caused by light which is not reflected from the subject entering the camera. Undersea photographers have discovered that about the best thing they can do to conquer the haze problem is to illuminate as little as possible of the water between the camera and the object they are

A hydrophone used in taking seismic surveys. To keep the ship's noise from interfering, the active hydrophone section (right) is towed 1,000 feet astern.

An electrically powered sound source is lowered into the ocean for an acoustic experiment.

photographing. Many ingenious rigs have been worked out which hold the lights and the camera so that both are brought close to the subject.

Many kinds of lights are used. In shallow water, a cable from the ship's power source can deliver current to continuously operated lamps. For deep-water pictures by cameras let down from ships, battery-powered flash bulbs or electronic flash discharge devices are used. The batteries providing the power are lowered along with the camera.

Sound plays a part in solving another baffling problem. How could the scientists aboard a ship, attempting to take pictures of a segment of the sea floor, tell when they

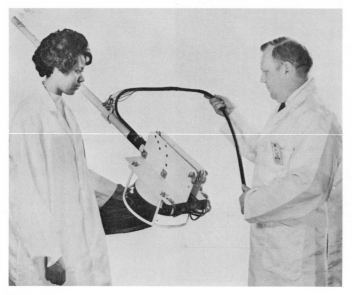

A sound source assembly so sensitive that it enabled M.I.T. researchers to identify the layering between tidal salt water and fresh water in the Charles River, Boston.

had the camera the proper distance from the floor? An unexpected hump in the sea floor could result in a damaged camera; a dip could mean pictures taken from too far away.

Dr. Harold Edgerton, of Massachusetts Institute of Technology and Woods Hole, a pioneer in undersea photography, solved this problem, as he did many others, to make the camera a more usable oceanographic instrument. His invention, called a "pinger," is essentially a device which sends out a series of pinging sounds as it descends. Some of the pings are received directly from the camera, some bounce off the sea floor. By comparing the time it takes these two sets of sound waves to reach the ship, the exact distance above the floor can be determined. In sophisticated versions, the camera is set to start taking pictures at a pre-determined height above the subject. So accurately can the camera be positioned by this photographic application of sonar that it can be lowered to within one foot of the sea floor.

Underwater camera sleds

"Would you mind losing a camera?" The words were those of Daniel Cousteau, the oceanographer father of Jacques-Yves Cousteau. Harold Edgerton, his companion on an oceanographic vessel plying the Mediterranean, answered laughingly, "No more than my right arm."

"Let's work up a sort of a sled and drag it across the bottom. Think a camera would stand a ride like that?" Cousteau asked.

The two men proceeded to make the world's first camera sled out of materials they had at hand. It consisted mainly of runners made from the curved hand rails of a diving ladder, with a plank laid between them. The camera was lashed to the plank. Suspending the sled by cable, they dragged it slowly across the sea floor off Tunisia. The camera came up intact—bringing with it amazing close-ups of the sea bottom.

Later the two ocean scientists designed a more sophisticated camera sled, equipped with a roll-over bar which permitted it to right itself if it was overturned. The runners were slightly crabbed outward so that mud stirred up by its passage did not obstruct the camera's view. The sled was cunningly designed to climb obstacles.

It soon proved its value as a means of giving science a close-up view of the sea floor. Cousteau was commissioned to survey a pipeline route across the Mediterranean. Drawing newly improved sleds across the

A sea bottom photography system. It can take 2,700 pictures during a single "dive."

"CURV," a machine equipped with sonar and television cameras, is used to find and recover objects from the sea floor. Controlled by cables from a surface ship, "CURV" can lift objects weighing as much as a ton.

115-mile stretch of sea, Cousteau's party came up with an inch-by-inch photographic record of many miles of sea floor. Engineers were subsequently able to select the best possible path for the pipeline built from North Africa to France.

Since then the sleds have been widely used in many undersea surveys, both in shallow and deep water. Attached to seven miles of steel cable, one was pulled along the bottom of the Puerto Rico Trench, deepest spot in the Atlantic. Motion picture cameras are

This picture of a brass pipe, twisted by the awesome deep-sea pressures that tore apart the submarine "Thresher," was another ocean bottom photo made by the "Trieste." The words "593 boat," barely visible near the bottom edge of the pipe, were conclusive evidence that the remains of the "Thresher" had been found. The nuclear sub's hull number was 593.

often used, and viewers of the ocean bottom movies describe the "startling" feeling they have, that they are moving along inches above the sea floor.

Many variations of the sled are being developed, so the ocean explorers of the late 60's find themselves provided with a wide choice of camera-carrying vehicles. A number of them are made by the firm of Edgerton, Germeshausen and Grier, with which Dr. Edgerton is associated. Others are developed for the special needs of different research organizations.

One of the most remarkable of these special sea-floor camera carriers is the "Cable Lowered Information Gathering System" developed at the U.S. Navy Electronics Laboratory in San Diego, California. Watertight cases enclose stereo cameras mounted on a sled-like frame. Special tripping mechan-isms and a pre-set programming device operate the cameras, strobe lights and other equipment. Positioned by the built-in sonar transducer, the sled can start taking pictures at any height, as well as on the bottom.

Underwater television

A submarine tragedy in 1951 led to the first successful use of underwater television. When the British submarine *Affray* sank in the Thames Estuary, the British Admiralty housed a television camera in a watertight casing and lowered it near the spot where the submarine was believed to lie. As the search ship moved along, watchers aboard it saw the word *Affray* flash onto the screen. The submarine, its name plainly visible, had been found. Unfortunately, all aboard her were dead, but television had begun its career as an oceanographic instrument.

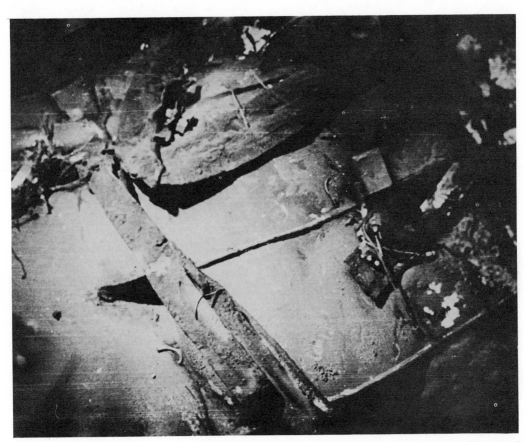

A photo made by the bathyscaph "*Trieste*" during the search for the sunken submarine "*Thresher*." The object in the photo was identified as part of a sonar dome used exclusively on "*Thresher*" class subs.

An underwater camera system is lowered gently into the sea.

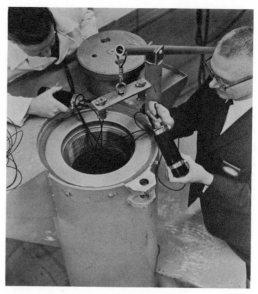

This cylinder was once a gun barrel on a Navy battleship. Now it is used as a high-pressure chamber to test new underwater instruments. Scientists are shown placing two deep-sea hydrophones in the cylinder. After the top is screwed on water is pumped in until the pressure is 250,000 pounds psi (per square inch)— equivalent to more than that at an 8-mile depth. Electrical apparatus outside records the effectiveness of the instruments being tested.

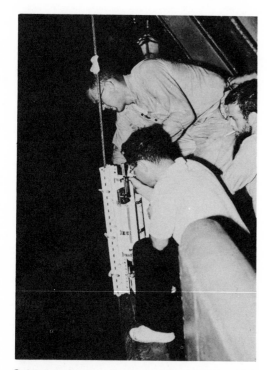

Scientists lower a "pinger." This device, which emits sound pulses and picks up echoes from the bottom, makes it possible to position cameras and other equipment at the desired distance above the sea floor.

This complex device is a thermometer specially made for recording deep-sea temperatures. It can accurately measure temperatures to one ten-thousandth of a degree at depths as great as 20,000 feet.

A unique tool which combines ocean bottom sampling and photography —a grab with a camera mounted on the top. Scientists use the photographs to determine the natural state of matter collected by the grab.

Since then, many different types of undersea television cameras have been developed, making TV an important tool for ocean research. Geologists prospecting the sea floor for minerals, marine biologists studying undersea life, fisheries researchers seeking to improve the catch—these are some of the scientists who regularly make use of underwater television. Many of the problems of lighting and control of the camera while underwater have been solved.

One of the most advanced underwater television systems has been developed by the U.S. Fish and Wildlife Service. Its camera is so sensitive that it can produce a clear image with only one foot-candle of light. Housed in a chamber that can withstand the pressure at 1,000 feet, it is controlled from the deck as it scans the depths. The operator can change its focus, and even bring into place his choice of three different lenses.

Biologists seated comfortably before the television screen—about the size of a living room set—have been able to learn many important facts about fish, which do not seem to mind the invasion of the camera into their domain.

Samples from the sea

Pictures from the sea are of great value to oceanographers, but to fully understand the ways of the ocean, the scientists must get actual samples of materials and creatures.

Many instruments have been designed for this purpose.

The corers. Scientists need to know the composition of the earth below the sea bottom. To find out, they use devices which are driven into the sea bottom to bring up a core—a cylinder of earth and rock. One of these is the Phleger Corer, which produces one-meter-long cores of bottom sediments. It drives itself into the sea floor by the force of its drop, and it is kept on course, pointed downwards, by a tailfin assembly. A plastic liner serves as a wrapper for the sample core.

Another widely used coring device is the Ewing Corer, developed by Dr. Maurice Ewing of the Lamont Geological Observatory. It ingeniously uses a piston to help the force of gravity pull the sample into the core pipe. It brings up huge samples as much as 59 feet long. Even this record is exceeded by the Kullenberg Corer, the giant of core samplers. This also uses hydrostatic pressure applied to a piston which can drive the corer as deep as 70 feet into the sea floor.

The grabs. To find out about the composition of the ocean bottom's surface, ocean scientists employ a variety of grab samplers. One is the "orange peel," which is so named because its four jaws are shaped like the skin of an orange when peeled in four equal longitudinal sections. The orange peel grab drags along the bottom, digging into sediment. As it is pulled along, its jaws close.

45

A new type of corer plunges to the ocean floor. It will extract a 5-foot-long cylindrical core from the sea bottom without disturbing its properties. The expendable plastic barrel (the long white portion) with its load of sediment is later removed, sliced up like a sausage, and analyzed in a lab.

A similar sampler is the "clamshell snapper," with two jaws shaped like clamshells. These jaws are operated by springs which are released when the snapper hits bottom. Various forms of dredges, some consisting of steel boxes open at one end, are dragged along the sea floor to gather samples as the research ship moves through the water.

The biological samplers. Marine biologists have developed many kinds of nets to bring up samples of living creatures from the sea. One, which captures the tiniest of sea creatures and plants, the microscopic plankton, is the Clark-Bumpus sampler. Towed behind a research vessel, it permits water to flow through a brass tube, retaining the plankton from the water in a nylon net. A recording device shows the exact amount of water that has flowed through the tube, information of importance to the biologist who is trying to find out just how rich this portion of the sea may be in the minute organisms that provide food for fish. The Hardy recorder, developed by Professor Alister Hardy of Oxford University, is similar in basic principle, but it can be towed by a ship moving at 15 knots.

For larger sea specimens, the marine biologists depend on variations of fishermen's nets. These nets, such as the Midwater Trawl, have devices fitted to them to keep them at depths pre-determined by the scientists.

Sea water samplers. Knowledge of the chemical composition of sea water is important to marine biologists. The method of getting samples for laboratory analysis has been little changed since the famous Arctic explorer, Fridtjof Nansen, invented the Nansen Bottle at the end of the last century. This useful device is essentially a tube-shaped metal cylinder or bottle with a valve at each end. The bottle is attached to a wire which carries it into the water. When the top end is released by a weight, which slides down the wire, the bottle reverses its position on the wire. When this happens, both valves close,

thus trapping a sample of the water at that particular depth. A number of Nansen bottles can be carried on a single wire, and set so that, as each bottle reverses, it releases a weight which trips the next bottle. Thus it is possible to obtain sea water samples at many different levels almost simultaneously.

Data from the depths

Not all information from the depths of the sea can be obtained in the form of photographs, "sound pictures," or samples. Much data must come in the form of readings on instruments that record various sea phenomena.

Magnetometers. Ore bodies beneath the surface create magnetic variations that can be measured by magnetometers. The sea-borne magnetometer is a remarkable device based on the fact that protons spin like tops in a magnetic field. The rate of spin is proportionate to the magnetic effect of the land below. The magnetometer used by ocean scientists is towed behind the ship to minimize the ship's effect on the sensitive instrument.

Gravity meters. The thickness and composition of the earth's crust below the sea can be revealed by various kinds of gravity meters. Most instruments are based on the principle of the weighted spring, the length of the spring varying with the gravitational pull. Instruments of this type once had to be lowered into the sea. Improved versions can now be housed aboard the ship.

Current meters. A research vessel ploughing through the water at a good 15 knots—measuring the speed of ocean currents as she goes—is a sight that would have amazed oceanographers a few years ago. What makes this feat possible is GEK (geomagnetic electro-kinetograph), which was developed by William von Arx, oceanographer of the Woods Hole Oceanographic Institution. Its operation is based on the fact that currents of water in their passage through the ocean generate electricity. The device consists of a pair of electrodes attached to an electrical cable and towed some 300 feet apart. The cable leads to a recorder aboard the ship, which indicates electrical voltages proportionate to the flow of the ocean currents through which the cable is moving.

Thermometers. Taking the sea's temperature has long been one of the oceanographer's prime tasks. Today it is more important than ever, revealing as it does a vast amount of

A technician attaches a Nansen bottle to a cable. The Nansen bottle is the standard tool for collecting sea water samples.

A technician selects a picture from one of the four television cameras carried by the "*Albatross IV*," a fisheries research ship. The console also controls the pan and tilt mechanisms of the cameras.

information about currents, sea life and sea water's sound conductivity. Many different types of thermometers have been developed, ranging from simple glass ones to electronic apparatus.

The most widely used is the device called BT by scientists, by which they mean the bathythermograph invented by Dr. Athelstan Spilhaus, now Dean of the Institute of Technology, University of Minnesota. It takes ocean temperature as it is towed by a ship. Its temperature-sensing element is a 50-foot-long copper tube filled with xylene, a fluid which expands and contracts with temperature change. These changes are transmitted to a stylus which provides a written record of temperature changes by making scratches on a metal-coated glass slide.

A host of new electrical thermometers have been developed. These "thermistors" translate temperature changes into electrical currents which can be registered on instruments aboard ship.

The largest oceanographic instrument is the thermistor chain, a giant weighing many tons, in which a large number of thermistors are placed. Many different types of thermistor

Scientists lower a chain dredge from the stern of the research ship "*Horizon*" into the choppy waters of the Gulf of Alaska. The "*Horizon*" is one of the many vessels in the oceanographic fleet operated by the Scripps Institution of Oceanography, La Jolla, California.

chains have been developed, but the biggest is that created by the technicians of the Navy Electronics Lab in San Diego. This 900-foot-long instrument consists of a chain constructed of large, flat links, each 12 inches long, 10 inches wide, and one inch thick. Fitted in grooves inside the flat links are 100 pairs of insulated wires, connected to temperature sensors called "thermistor beads," placed at 27-foot intervals on the chain.

In use, the chain is lowered from the stern of the oceanographic ship. A 2,300-pound "fish," a heavy metal weight, causes it to sink. As the ship sails, the thermistor beads send up continuous signals to indicate the temperature of the water. These signals are scanned electronically every 10 seconds, and lines showing the depths of the temperatures are printed on 19-inch wide tape. Also printed on the same tape is the depth of the "fish" and the temperature of the sea surface.

4. FOOD FROM THE SEA

In a world menaced by hunger, less than 1 per cent of all food comes from the sea. Yet the world's oceans could be man's most bounteous source of nourishment. Many urgent projects to explore and exploit the sea's food resources are now underway in almost every country in the world that borders on the sea. Also, the United Nations, through the FAO (the Food and Agricultural Organization), is sponsoring several international projects.

Scientists are spurred on by the knowledge that food from the sea could do far more than simply make up the 20,000,000-ton protein shortage that exists today. Many scientists believe that the sea, if properly used, could provide a huge surplus of vital protein, producing two to twenty times the present yield. Many possibilities present themselves—improved ways to find, catch and preserve fish; the creation of new kinds of fish by breeding; fish farming; agriculture to raise plants in the sea. What science does to realize these potentialities can spell the difference between starvation or adequate nutrition for millions of people.

Finding the fish

"You can't catch fish you can't find," is an axiomatic statement. To help the fishermen find the fish, scientists are studying fish habits, trying to trace their movements through the seas. Tagging is a major means of finding out about distances and routes traversed by fish. Way back in 1653, Isaak Walton first tagged fish by tying colored ribbons to their tails so he could better observe their movement through the water. The purpose of today's scientific tagging is not observation of fish in motion, since that would be impossible over long distances in the sea. The modern technique is to tag a fish at a given spot, then record the place where the fish is caught. Fishermen co-operate with scientists by send-

Underwater chambers permit close-up study of fish in action.

(Above) The camera case is shown attached to a trawl (A and B). The floats (C) are part of the trawl used in fisheries research. (Below) One of the photographs made by this towed camera.

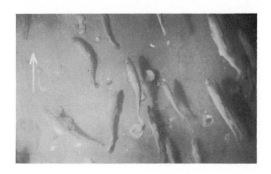

A marine biologist prepares a multi-flash camera (A) for fisheries research work. It will be pulled in a trawl. Parts shown are: electronic flash (B), waterproof case (C), buoyancy tubes (D) to reduce weight in water.

ing the tag they find to the address stamped on it.

Scientific fish taggers have developed many ways of marking fish. One widely used marker is the Peterson tag, which consists of two bright plastic discs fastened by a metal pin through back muscles. Another type is the Gilbert strip, a metal clip quickly fastened to tail fin, mouth, or gill with a special pair of pliers developed by Dr. C. H. Gilbert of Stanford University, California. Salmon are tagged by marking an incision in the fish's belly and inserting a strip of plastic. When the fish is processed at the cannery, the tag comes to light.

Tagging some fish presents baffling problems for the marine biologists. They found that the blue tuna, for instance, was so exhausted after it was brought to a boat and tagged that it became easy prey for sharks when released. The researchers overcame this difficulty by ingeniously letting the tuna tag themselves. The tag is a baited hook attached to piano wire. When the tuna strikes, the wire holds just long enough for the hook to sink in, then breaks.

Of course, only a few of the tagged fish are ever recovered, but it is not necessary to have a large number of recoveries to provide an adequate sampling. In the case of salmon, where millions are tagged annually, a 2 per cent return is more than enough to give the scientists the information they seek. Occasionally, they are surprised at the large percentage of return. Of 7,600 skipjacks tagged off Hawaii, 633 were picked up.

While tagging is the best method of determining long range movements of fish, it does not solve the problem of locating particular schools of fish. The most widely used device for short-range fish detection is the echo sounder, in the form known as Asdic. It uses sound-producing oscillators which send out the sound horizontally. The waves strike fish and are returned to the ship. Large schools of fish can be identified at distances up to 2 miles. In a typical successful use of this type of sound-detecting equipment, a Norwegian fishing craft located a school of herring and made an enormous catch at a time when other ships not so equipped were reporting poor catches. Scientists have reported following a school of fish for hundreds of miles with the aid of sound.

Aircraft are coming into use for spotting fish. Visual sightings can often be made by aerial observers. Airborne radar can detect minute disturbances on the surface of the water caused by fish swimming close beneath it. Another valuable instrument is an infrared detector which indicates the currents of warmer water that fish like to follow.

The submarine may soon become a practical tool for fishermen. The U.S. Bureau of Commercial Fisheries has designed a nuclear-powered research submarine capable of moving at 20 knots, keeping tabs on schools of fish at any reasonable depth. The U.S.S.R. has developed two deep-sea scouting vessels to hunt out fish underwater. One is the *Sever-II*, described as "somewhat of a cross between *Alvin* and *Aluminaut*." The midget craft, designed to carry two men, has only a single large viewing port, but it is equipped with an unusual arrangement of floodlights.

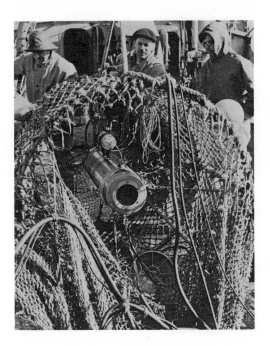

One is above the viewing port pointing downwards, and the other two are placed in 12-foot booms which can be swung out to deliver light as far as 45 feet, making possible visual observations of fish in deep, dark waters. Sensitive sonar apparatus permits location of more distant fish.

Satellites in outer space may become fish-finders in the near future. In the U.S., the Bureau of Commercial Fisheries has been working with the National Aeronautics and Space Administration in experiments aimed at using space craft for this purpose. Scientists of both organizations report themselves "encouraged" by their tests. Instruments aboard satellites circling the earth every hour or so could keep constant track of fishing conditions on any part of the globe. Sensitive variations of the infra-red detectors and radar could do for large areas of the sea what these instruments do for small areas when carried by aircraft.

Science goes fishing

Many scientists are fascinated by the idea of using electricity to catch fish. This possibility is based on observation by researchers that fish will swim towards the source of a strong electric current. A number of experiments have been carried out by fisheries experts of the U.S., Great Britain, Germany, the U.S.S.R., and several other countries.

One of the promising types of apparatus has been developed by the German engineers, Hans Rump and Karl Heinz Ulrichs. Their equipment consists of an underwater electrode which, connected to a generator on the fishing vessel, sends out intermittent currents which spread out in the water. A pipe extending down from the ship terminates near the electrode. As fish encounter the current, they are drawn irresistibly toward the electrode, electrocuted, and then sucked up into the pipe, which runs to tanks in the vessel.

In demonstrations of the Rump-Ulrichs device, a catch that would take hours with nets was gathered in minutes. In one test, 2,000 pounds of fish were swept into the

Television camera used in underwater study of fish and other marine life goes overboard inside a large trawling net.

A new $2,000,000 fisheries research vessel, the "*Albatross IV*," riding at anchor at Woods Hole, Mass., her home port.

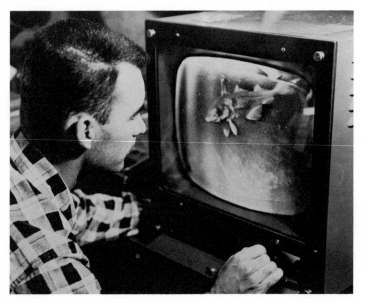

Fisheries scientist aboard the "*Albatross IV*" gets a close-up view of fish in their natural habitat. Pictures are made by underwater camera connected by cable to the ship.

Collecting data on the size and distribution of sea scallops aboard the "*Albatross IV.*"

pipe in less than 5 minutes. The apparatus is inexpensive to operate, since it requires a generator with a capacity of less than 500 kilowatts.

Another lure for fish is sound. Many studies have revealed that the sea, far from being the quiet place it once was thought to be, is filled with many sounds made by marine life. Studies at the Narragansett Marine Laboratory in Massachusetts revealed that of 60 fishes studied all but 6 make detectable sounds.

Fish have many ways of making sounds— by vibrating the gas bladder, scraping teeth together, vibrating bones, and rubbing pectoral fins along the body. The sounds they emit have been described as drum-like, scraping, rasping, whining, and scratching; as thumps, grunts, groans, growls, knocks, thuds, clicks, and barks.

When scientists succeed in sorting out the meanings of these sounds, they believe they can put them to work to attract, or drive, fish to fishing boats. Dr. Columbus Iselin, the Woods Hole oceanographer, has suggested that sounds that frighten fish could be used. He pictures a ship equipped to emit the same sounds as those produced by fish which are predators of the particular kind of fish being sought. The tail beats of predator fish, he suggests, must be well known to their potential victims. A vessel sending the menacing sound of that tail beat into the water could be used to drive whole schools of fish towards fishing craft with waiting nets.

Research by other scientists is directed toward utilizing the chemical senses of fishes to increase the sea's yield of food. Typical are the researches of Dr. C. E. Lucas of the Fisheries Research Laboratories, Aberdeen, Scotland. Dr. Lucas discovered that chemicals play a part in the ability of salmon to find their way back to the river in which they were spawned. He found that the fish were capable of recognizing, by a combined sense of smell and taste, the chemicals peculiar to a particular river. When these were present in sea water in dilutions of one part in many millions, they could follow the "trail" of these chemicals to the river. Naturally, these chemicals would be more abundant as they neared the mouth of the river.

Marine biologists are sure that many other substances associated with food, survival and mating, are sensed by fish. Admittedly, science has a long way to go before it can capitalize on these amazing chemical senses, but a number of possibilities are being explored. They fall into two categories. One uses attractant chemicals to draw the fish toward fishing vessels or particular estuaries where nets are waiting. The other concept is to use chemicals which are repelling to fish. They then swim away from the areas in which it was dropped in, say, a semi-circular pattern. This in effect, creates a chemical net, driving the fish toward the waiting ships.

53

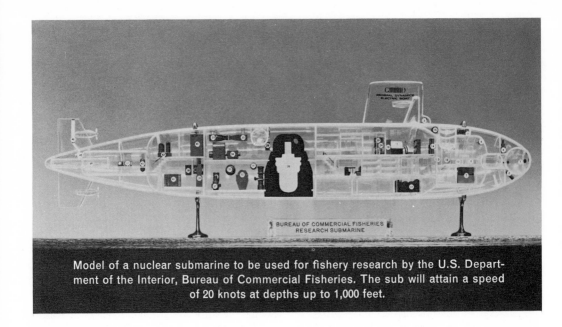

Model of a nuclear submarine to be used for fishery research by the U.S. Department of the Interior, Bureau of Commercial Fisheries. The sub will attain a speed of 20 knots at depths up to 1,000 feet.

Fish farming

Despite all the progress in fishing methods, many marine biologists believe that seeking out fish in the wide oceans is an inefficient and primitive way to extract fish from the sea. They liken it to the pre-agricultural stage of man's existence, when early man had not learned to domesticate animals and grow crops, but instead had to hunt for his food. These critical scientists believe that we must turn to *mariculture*, sea farming, raising fish in ponds or closed-off portions of the sea.

The arguments for fish farming are many. There is, to begin with, the fantastic mortality rate of fish. The mackerel may be taken as an example. The loss of these fish from the moment of spawning to the time they reach a mere 2 inches in size, is calculated at 99.9996 per cent! The difference between a good and a bad year for mackerel fishermen is determined by a 2 per cent change in the survival rate of the fish. Disease, predators and availability of food, are a few among many factors—all beyond human control in the open sea.

Fish farming could establish control over all these factors. Not only would the fish be able to multiply freely, but they would be far more easily harvested, without search, and with apparatus far more efficient and inexpensive than fishing vessels.

Fish farming is far from new. In many parts of the world, particularly in the Orient, it is widely practiced, with remarkable results. Fish farms on the shores of Taiwan (Formosa), for instance, produce 1,200 pounds of fish per acre, with several "crops" a year possible. Japan, perhaps the most advanced of all nations in fish farming, tops this record consistently. Estimates by U.S. marine biologists place the possible yield of fish farms in closed-off inlets along the U.S. east coast at 6,000 pounds per acre.

Comparing fish farm yields to those of land acres, Dr. Lionel Walford, of the Fishery Biology Branch of the U.S. Fish and Wildlife Service, states: "With the same kind of care that farmland requires, that is, careful selection of stock, fertilizing, feeding, and removal of predators, a brackish pond can produce better than three times as much flesh as can an acre of land. This is by using present information. What might result if as much research were put into brackish pond farming as has already gone into agriculture, no one can say."

One of the problems that engages scientists and engineers in creating a fish farm is the question of where to put it. In certain areas the conformity of the coast makes it easy to let sea water into ponds. In other coastal areas, closing off tidal inlets is more promising. For ponds, simple dams may suffice;

large inlets, or arms of the sea, where dams would be too expensive or difficult to build, will require methods not at present used in fish culture.

Engineers have made many suggestions. Some have proposed using electricity, creating a shock barrier that would admit the water, but not let the cultivated fish out or the predators in. Others propose using a curtain of sound, which would have similar effects. Woods Hole oceanographers have conducted extensive experiments with a third method which appears to be inexpensive and effective. They have found that fish shy away from air bubbles. Utilizing this knowledge, the scientists have laid down perforated plastic pipes or hoses into which they fed compressed air. No fish would swim through the bubbling water.

These same devices would make it possible to carry out another dream of the proponents of mariculture—fencing off areas of the open sea. Barriers of sound or air bubbles could be made to cover hundreds, or even thousands, of acres, where millions of fish could be grown. Engineers picture such sea enclosures being tended, not by ships, but by permanently established floating platforms like those used for offshore oil drilling. These platforms would house complete factories for processing fish, as well as equipment for harvesting fish which, selectively attracted by sound or chemicals, would deliver themselves to the factory.

Jacques-Yves Cousteau, the tireless French sea researcher, proposes underwater buildings for fish farms. In his many underwater excursions he often noticed the large numbers of fish that used sunken ships as their "homes." Why not design structures that would provide habitats for fish? His answer to that question is the *Biatron*, a concrete building with several floors, each one equipped to accommodate and attract a particular species of fish. Cousteau visualizes a system of pipes to deliver chemical nutrients to the fish.

Atomic energy to provide more fish

Even if science succeeds in enormously increasing the quantity of fish yielded by the sea, there is a troubling problem. To meet the world's growing food needs, fish must be delivered free of harmful bacteria to undeveloped parts of the world, where modern deep-freeze facilities are not available.

Atomic energy may prove one key to providing protein-rich seafood for the undernourished peoples of those areas. It may also widen the use of seafood in more prosperous countries, providing such treats as fresh oysters all year round, and fresh fish, rather than frozen, in places far inland.

The secret is irradiation, bombarding seafood with radioactive rays. As explained by Drs. John D. Kaylor and Joseph H. Slavin, of the U.S. Bureau of Commercial Fisheries, Gloucester, Massachusetts: "Radioactive cobalt is the key to this new method of pasteurizing foods. Cobalt-60 constantly emits invisible electromagnetic rays similar to X-rays, but of even shorter wave length. Called gamma rays, they possess extraordinary penetrating power. These rays kill or inactivate about 99 per cent of the bacteria normally found in fish fillets."

The basic process of irradiation to kill

A scientist checks the growth rate of oysters on a controlled diet.

A 650-pound catch of royal red shrimp is hauled aboard.

bacteria was discovered by the late Dr. E. B. Proctor, of the Massachusetts Institute of Technology, who succeeded in sterilizing beef with high energy X-rays. However, at the start, his process killed the taste as well as the bacteria. Later experiments carried out by Dr. Proctor and his associates, in co-operation with the Atomic Energy Commission, revealed that the more deeply penetrating rays given off by radioactive substances, such as cobalt-60, did not affect the taste. Dr. Proctor suggested that the radiation be applied to fish.

In 1964, a large irradiator was constructed by the AEC at the Gloucester Laboratories. The heart of the irradiator is a massive structure with walls 5 feet thick. The rest of the building houses a refrigerated area and a conveyor that carries packages of fish to be irradiated through an underground labyrinth and then up into the radiation cell. Each package of fish moves past the block of cobalt-60 four times to receive the 250,000 rad (a rad is a unit of radiation) required to sterilize it.

A report on the success of this irradiator states that the normal refrigerated shelf life of shrimp, haddock, cod, ocean perch, flounder, sole, halibut and other fish is doubled or tripled. Exposure to radioactivity does not affect the food.

Other experimental irradiators have been developed which can be used aboard ships. Atomic Energy of Canada has produced one

which can be housed on a truck or sent to sea. It is probable that, in the near future, fish will be irradiated as soon as caught.

Fish flour

FPC—fish protein concentrate—is one of the brightest hopes for a protein-hungry world. Developed by chemists of the U.S. Bureau of Commercial Fisheries, it is a fine white powder produced by chemical and electrical processes from whole fish—any kind of fish. Tasteless and without aroma, in one form it looks like ordinary wheat flour. It also comes as a plain milk-like liquid, and as a paste. It is as rich in food value as meat, eggs or milk, yet it costs only a fraction of these expensive protein foods. Pilot plant experiments indicate that it may be produced for as little as 3¢ a pound. FPC can be used in any of the ways grain flours are used, or as a food supplement added to any food. Its use involves no change in national dietary habits, so it has no regional prejudices to overcome, as is the case when people who do not customarily eat fish are offered it in a natural form.

Scientists estimate that FPC could be produced in almost unlimited quantities, for it can be made from any kind of fish. Fully half of the fish caught by commercial fishermen are considered useless and thrown back into the sea. These fish make just as good FPC as the popular varieties. Moreover, the fish concentrate makes full use of the fish. Some

Six pounds of fish produce one pound of fish flour, a protein-rich food which could ease the world's food problems.

people have objected to this, but scientists point out that the concentrate is completely purified during processing. Also, they remind the objectors, people eat whole sardines, anchovies and oysters without a thought.

At present FPC is being made in shore-based experimental plants, but in the future there is no reason why it should not be made at sea. Dr. D. L. McKerran, Director of the U.S. Bureau of Commercial Fisheries, suggests that fish could be ground up and processed aboard the fishing boat while it moved about the fishing grounds and voyaged home. "When the vessel got back to port," concludes Dr. McKerran, "it would have a liquid mass in its hold. It could be pumped out, spray-dried and packaged."

Seaweed for food

When Dr. Hirois Tamiya, a Japanese scientist, invited some of his colleagues in California to lunch, he served them soup, noodles, rolls, tea and ice cream. All these foods were made from algae! Although the particular algae he used in preparing his unusual lunch did not come from the sea, they could have. For some of the giant algae we know as seaweeds are good to eat.

So far, science has found some forty different uses for seaweed extracts in the food, pharmaceutical and textile industries, and researchers are sure they will find many more. Algin, agar and carrageenin (or Irish moss), three versatile substances extracted from seaweed, have many applications in food. They are commonly used in so many processed foods that you almost certainly have eaten some seaweed recently. Because of their unique properties as stabilizers, seaweed extracts are used in ice cream, malted milk, cheese, chocolate milk, puddings, mayonnaise, salad dressing, and jellies.

These food uses of seaweed are not based on what many researchers like Dr. Tamiya consider to be the most important quality of seaweed—its nutritional value. Seaweeds contain carbohydrates, protein, minerals and many vitamins. In Norway, Great Britain, and Germany, meal made from ground-up brown kelp is widely used as an animal food. It is also incorporated in various "health" breads, in which bakers use the seaweed meal as a nutritional supplement. Experiments in using this meal as a fertilizer for land crops open up another way in which seaweed might help increase the world's food supply.

Economics pose the major problem to a wider use of seaweed. The high costs of harvesting and processing offset many advantages. If scientists and engineers can find ways to cut costs, the quantities of seaweed available are staggering. In one study of a 2,500-acre sea area off Nova Scotia, for example, researchers estimate that there are 80,000 tons of seaweed. Its density, in places, is as high as 57 tons per acre. If harvested, these waters would grow several crops a year.

Why not grow seaweed as a crop? Again economics stands in the way. However, the Japanese are successfully pioneering seaweed cultivation. In shallow seaside ponds they plant microscopic seaweed seeds in handy, inexpensive "pots" also provided by the sea—empty clam shells. Later, the seaweed is transplanted to nets in the water, where it grows so rapidly that it can be harvested in two months. Thus a given area of the sea is made to produce as many as six crops a year.

In the U.S.S.R., ocean scientists have conducted extensive experiments in seaweed

A shore-based fisheries researcher adjusts the chromatograph he is using to analyze the taste components of sea foods.

cultivation. While the harvesting problem has not been solved, the Russian scientists freely predict it will be.

"By the year 2,000 the new science of submarine agronomy will be with us," says one report. "Sea farmers will harvest down to a depth of 300 feet in diving vessels assisted by remote control harvesters to obtain useful plants in these growing seaweed forests."

"Surely," says Dr. Athelstan Spilhaus, Dean of the Institute of Technology, University of Minnesota, "just as the grasses of the land were developed to yield the wheat, corn, barley, rice, rye, oats, and even sugar for our daily 'bread,' seaweed can be cultivated to form an important part of our food."

The promise of plankton

Are fish and seaweed the best form of food from the sea? Many scientists do not think so. They believe that there is a far richer source of sea-food—plankton, the microscopic plants and animals that swarm in sea water, turning it into what has been called "the nutritious soup of the sea."

The word "plankton" means (in Greek, from which it is derived) "that which is made

to wander." The *phytoplankton*, the plants, are made up of two main groups, the diatoms and the flagellates. Diatoms come in a fantastic variety of shapes, including rectangles, rods, needles, and intricate cylinders shaped like pill boxes. The flagellates have two or more whip-like appendages, which, when moved rapidly about, cause the flagellate to be propelled through the water. Scientists do not agree as to whether these strange creatures should be classed as plants, animals or both.

The other components of the sea's living soup are the *zooplankton*, which are unmistakably animals. The most numerous type of these minute animals are the "oar-footed" creatures called copepods. Professor Alister Hardy, of Oxford University, states: "It is no exaggeration to say that in the plankton may be found an assemblage of animals more diverse and more comprehensive than is to be seen in any other realm of life." In terms of numbers, too, the plankton must be described in superlatives. It is estimated that there are more copepods in the world than all other multi-celled creatures combined, *including insects!*

These tiny animals feed on the phytoplankton to start what is called "the food chain of the sea." The next link in the chain is created when small fish, such as herring,

A technician monitors the control of a powerful irradiator used in preservation of fish.

58

eat the plankton. Next, a still larger fish, say a tuna, eats the herring. Man forges the final link when he eats the tuna.

Sea scientists believe that the richest promise of the seas as a source of food lies in finding a way to shorten that chain. They point out that the chain, as described, represents a tremendous loss of food value. It takes 1,000 pounds of diatoms to create 100 pounds of zooplankton, which in turn create 10 pounds of herring, which create 1/10th of a pound of tuna.

Find a way to gather the highly nutritious plankton and turn it directly into food for man, the scientists reason, and a food supply for even the most grossly overpopulated world would be assured.

In what form could man eat plankton, and what would it taste like? People who have eaten it raw, just as it comes from the ocean, or boiled like an ordinary meat or vegetable, have varying opinions. Thor Heyerdahl and his five companions, who drifted across the Pacific from Peru to Polynesia on a raft, the *Kon Tiki*, supplemented their diets with plankton on their 4,800-mile voyage. They described some of it as tasting like caviar,

Marine biologists engaged in improving fisheries do much laboratory work. Here they are examining haddock for indications of maturity and time of spawning.

A bacteriologist studies the organisms that lead to the spoilage of fish.

oysters, lobster and shrimp. It seems unlikely that plankton will be widely eaten in anything like its original form. Most scientists suggest that it will be ground up to make a powder or flour, or a hamburger-like "meat." Many who have sampled it in this form have pronounced it tasty. However, by present methods of gathering plankton, the cost of a single planktonburger comes to around $3 or £1!

The trouble is that even in an area rich in plankton, it would be necessary to strain vast quantities of water to extract it. It has been calculated that to obtain an amount of plankton equalling the quantity of herring caught by an average fishing vessel in 100 hours—about 59 tons—it would be necessary to strain 57,500,000 tons of water. Any currently known means of processing that much water would take far too much power to be economical.

Professor Hardy at one time conducted an experiment which, he believed, might tap a power source of low enough cost—the tides.

An experimental cobalt-60 irradiator to be used aboard fishing vessels so that fish can be irradiated with gamma rays immediately after being caught, and then kept without refrigeration.

He suggested that nets across narrow tidal inlets could gather plankton during the 12 hours that the tide was running. The nets, based on the Hardy plankton net which is used by oceanographers in gathering small samples, would each, he figured, capture the plankton in 22,000 tons of sea water an hour. He estimated that each net could provide enough food for 3.75 persons. However, tests revealed that the nets were not efficient enough, nor was there a uniform enough amount of plankton to bear out Professor Hardy's calculations.

Despite setbacks, scientists are continuing to attack the problem. To spur them on, they have the example of nature's own filtering system as it exists in the blue whale. This giant creature which, when full grown, needs 1,000,000 calories a day, gets all of its food from the plankton it scoops up as it moves through the water. It has drastically shortened the food chain. Professor Hardy visualizes nuclear-powered, man-made "whales," ships that would pour a steady stream of plankton into their holds as they ply the seas.

By the turn of the century he predicts, "plankton may be making the greatest addition to man's food supply."

5. UNDERWATER MINING FOR MINERAL RICHES

On and under the sea floor is a vast treasure trove of mineral wealth. Some of it lies exposed, ready to be scooped up. Some of it is buried under earth and rocks, as are most of the minerals on land.

These undersea riches are a tempting target in the new field of oceanology. Right now, in many parts of the World Ocean, scientists and engineers are busy probing the exciting possibilities in underwater mining. Their promising start indicates a dazzling future.

Undersea gold rush

In the 19th century, the world was often thrilled by news of a great gold strike. California . . . Alaska and the Yukon . . . Australia . . . fortunes for prospectors and miners. Yet the greatest gold finds of all may be made in the second half of the 20th century—not on dry land, but under the sea. For science and technology are teaming up to search for and extract the gold that geologists believe lies on or under the sea floor.

The idea that there is gold under the sea is not a new one. Miners have long speculated about underwater gold. However, any such talk remained purely speculative until just a few years ago. Individual prospectors could not go looking for gold under the sea, as they did on land, and even big mining companies showed little interest in overcoming the problems of extracting gold from beneath the ocean floor.

The modern undersea gold rush had its beginnings in 1960 when two petroleum engineers employed by Shell Oil Company happened to land their light plane in Nome, Alaska. With some time on their hands, they looked around this little town, which had once been the scene of a great gold rush. Something the engineers saw attracted their interest. It was an old beach, from which the sea had receded, leaving it inland. They noticed that it showed many signs of having been dug up. When the visitors made inquiries in the town, old-timers told them that, years before, gold seekers had found millions in gold there.

What about the beaches that were underwater? Had anybody ever hunted there for gold? No one in Nome knew anything about any efforts to find the precious mineral under the cold waters. However, long ago, at the

A scientist starts a Peterson grab sampler on its trip to the ocean floor. On striking the bottom the sampler will trip and close. This is one of the standard tools used in all phases of oceanographic research.

Diamond-bearing gravel, sucked up from the ocean floor, is processed aboard the "*Colpontoon*." Screens sift out the diamonds (bottom left), the waste material pouring back into the sea (right).

end of the last century, some Western Union Telegraph engineers, laying a cable from Alaska to Siberia, had reported finding some flakes of gold in the offshore sands.

The Shell engineers made a routine report to their company: maybe it would pay to look into this business of gold in the shallow waters off Nome. A Shell geologist agreed, and after studying the possibilities, advised his company to get a prospecting permit from the State of Alaska to make the first big scientific search for undersea gold.

Prospecting for ocean gold

The oil company prospectors began their search with a seismic survey to determine the nature of underwater formations. Such a survey is performed with a "sparker" boat, a craft with apparatus that emits high intensity electric sparks. These sparks produce underwater sound waves which are reflected back from different surfaces on and under the ocean bottom. They enable scientists to "see" just what lies under the ocean floor. In this case, they were looking for ancient river channels which might have become filled in with silt. They also wanted to spot old beaches which had once been high and dry.

After months of seismic work, the prospectors were ready for the next activity, which took place in winter when the water was covered with a thick sheet of ice. On to this ice the geologists, aided by Eskimos, took a drilling rig. The 30-inch-thick ice served as a platform that safely supported the heavy equipment while its powerful drill dug through the ice, deep into the sea floor at spots the survey had indicated as promising. The samples of undersea gravel they drilled out were brought to the waiting men by compressed air. Taken ashore and panned (much in the manner that the sourdoughs of the last century sifted gravel), the value of the gold in the samples was calculated.

Naturally, the company has not revealed exactly what it found in these sampling operations, which have now gone on for several years. However, early in the proceedings, the company leased 5,120 underwater acres and has since leased an undisclosed number of additional acres. Dredging operations to bring up the gravel are underway. There is some outside speculation that a 5,120-acre area could yield 300 *tons* of gold. Deducting the highest cost likely for bringing up the gravel and processing it to extract the gold, the sea miners could derive a profit of $150,000,000 from this watery acreage.

No wonder many companies are joining in a scramble to prospect parts of the sea that scientists believe may contain gold. And no wonder geologists like Dr. Willard Bascom, the man who planned the Mohole (see next chapter), and who is now head of Ocean Science and Engineering, are freely predicting that the great gold strikes of the 1970's will be made underwater.

Diamonds under the sea

Diamonds from the sea?

For 25 years the idea that these precious stones could be found underwater was only the romantic dream of a British engineer named Peter Keeble. It began when Keeble, who had worked for construction companies in India, arrived in South Africa in the early 1930's. Fascinated by stories he had heard of a few diamonds being found near the mouths of rivers, he began to wonder if there might not be many more farther out at sea.

Experts shook their heads. The diamonds found underwater, they were sure, had simply been washed down from inland mountains. There might be diamonds under the sea, all right, but they would probably be buried far too deep under the sea floor to be found.

The young engineer was unconvinced. He made a number of experimental dives and brought up many samples of gravel that contained diamonds—not very big ones, nor many, but enough to make him feel he was on the right track. However, all his efforts to

A diamond dredge working in the Atlantic off the southern coast of Africa.

The U.S. Bureau of Mines research complex at Tiburon, California, where extensive underseas mining studies are carried out.

interest the big diamond mining companies were in vain.

After World War II, during which Keeble served with distinction in the British Navy, he took up his dream again. As before, the experts advised him to forget about the idea. It was 1959 when an American construction man, Sammy Collins, who had won fame as a builder of underwater pipelines, heard of Keeble's scheme. A bold and enterprising Texan who had often tackled jobs deemed impossible by others, Collins was so impressed by Keeble's theories that he proposed to set up a company to mine underwater diamonds. For both men it was a desperate gamble. Collins had just lost a fortune on a pipeline project in Iraq, and Keeble had almost lost hope that he would ever find a backer.

Barge 77—pioneer diamond ship

What kind of a craft should they use to scrape diamonds from the sea? To start with, Collins and Keeble chose a battered salvage tug, the *Emerson K*, and fitted her with a

lifting device which would claw up samples. In this vessel they set out on a prospecting voyage along the coast of southwest Africa, where Keeble had long believed diamonds were to be found.

When the *Emerson K*'s creaking hoist first began to bring up mud and gravel from the sea bottom, 100 feet below, the prospect looked as discouraging as the diamond experts had predicted. Even to find out if there were any diamonds in it, they had to put the drab sea earth through several processes. First they fed it to vibrating screens which removed mud. The gravel that was left was fed through other screens. Then the geologists and crewmen sorted by hand. But they did find diamonds! To be sure, they had to go through material a million times greater in quantity than the handful of precious stones they found, but better equipment, they knew, could simplify the process.

The better equipment came in the form of *Barge 77*, the world's first diamond-harvesting ship. A converted Collins trenching barge,

"*Deepstar-4000*," an advanced design diving saucer.

Scuba is an important tool in exploiting the riches of the sea.

A

Artist's conception of submarine drilling.

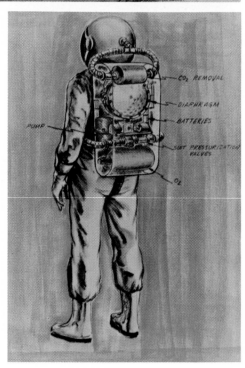

Advanced diving suit and gear being tested in
water-filled chamber.

B

The pressure hulls of "*Deep Quest*" during final welding.

"*Deep Quest*," a submarine developed for scientific undersea exploration.

An undersea workboat designed to carry out a variety of tasks.

The bathyscaph "*Trieste II*" being lowered into the sea.

Interior of the pioneer research submarine, "*Aluminaut*."

Oil-hunting geologists obtain valuable information about earth formations under the sea by measuring speed of sound waves from underwater explosions.

A cable-lowered information gathering device which includes a stereoscopic camera and other instruments.

F

From this man-made island sulphur is extracted from the sea.

A pile of golden sulphur which was pumped up from deposits beneath the sea floor.

G

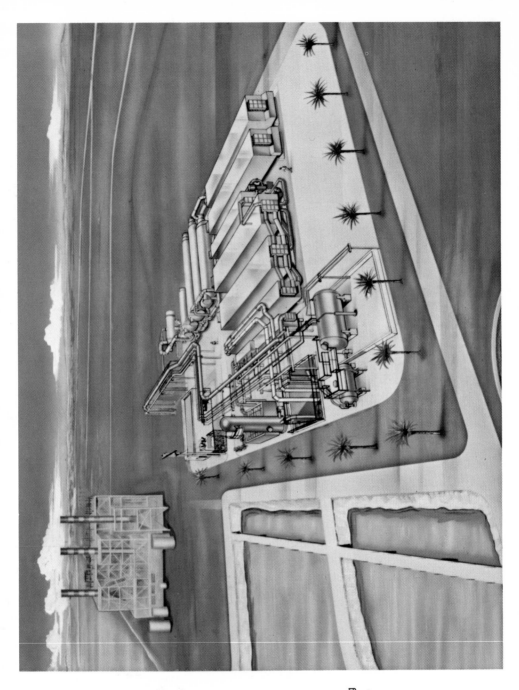

Sea water desalting plant at San Diego, California.

H

she was a much bigger craft than the *Emerson K*, capable of staying at sea for three months with a crew of 53.

A nozzle moving along the sea floor sprayed air at a pressure of 100 pounds to the square inch, stirring up the sand and gravel, which was then sucked into a pipe 12 inches in diameter. The pipe spewed out its potential treasure on to a conveyor belt, which carried it to the first of seven different machines for agitating, filtering, and scrubbing.

Soon *Barge 77* was amazing the world with its fabulous finds. On land, in the great diamond mines which were considered rich, it was necessary to move 95,000,000 pounds of material to recover a single average diamond of 1.19 carats. *Barge 77* was bringing up 4 carats for every 2,000 pounds of material!

Diamantkus

The career of *Barge 77* ended in a storm which tore her loose from her anchors and hurled her to destruction on a rocky shore. However, the lessons learned aboard her were incorporated in a new diamond-mining craft, *Barge 111*. New, more powerful machinery speeded up the lifting of material from the sea floor, and *Barge 111* soon outstripped the record of old *77*.

Meanwhile, the sea floor treasure seekers had started constructing the first ship designed specially for retrieving diamonds. This is the huge *Diamantkus*, which has been described as "looking more like a factory than a ship." The 300-foot craft has several levels of structural steel towering over its hull, and a tangle of pipes and hoses hanging over its side. Through them the pay dirt is sucked up from the sea at the rate of 300 tons an hour.

Diamantkus operates 24 hours a day, 7 days a week. Storms hold no terrors for the huge ship. With 6 mighty, 5-ton anchors to hold her firmly in place, she is capable of riding out 50-foot swells.

Other, even bigger, more elaborately equipped diamond ships are going into operation, among them *Ontinger I*. Though it has much more equipment aboard, and a far bigger capacity, *Ontinger I* requires a crew of only 17 because it is almost completely auto-

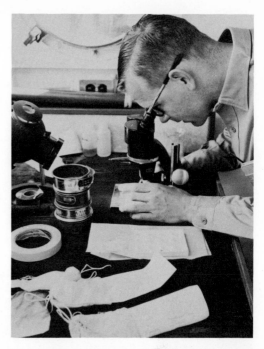

A scientist examines an undersea mineral specimen in the laboratory aboard the research vessel *"Cripple Creek."*

mated. Its more powerful suction equipment can work at depths much greater than the 100 feet or so to which earlier diamond ships were limited, so it is tapping new areas of the sea floor.

Tin

Geologists believe that some day all the different kinds of minerals that have been extracted from mines on dry land will be found under the sea floor.

One of the most sought-after minerals in the world is tin, the bluish-white metallic element. It has hundreds of uses in modern industry, ranging from coatings for "tin" cans (which are made of steel covered with tin), to alloys for bearings in automobiles and other machinery. Since tin is found in rather few places in the world, it is big news that the submarine prospectors are discovering huge new deposits of tin under the sea.

Seaborne prospectors are at work in many different coastal areas. For centuries tin has been mined in Cornwall, England, from mines that have gone ever deeper into the earth. Dwindling supplies of tin-bearing ore

The "*Grass Valley*", a former U.S. Navy submarine tender, has been converted to an undersea mining research vessel for the U.S. Department of Interior's Bureau of Mines.

have made mining more and more difficult and expensive. Now new deposits found in gravels of St. Ives Bay give promise of keeping tin mining alive in Cornwall.

Many other promising undersea sources of tin have been found off Asian coasts. For instance, a number of large British and American companies have been conducting extensive prospecting operations in the waters off Thailand. In one place large deposits of ores that bear tin have been found as far as 5 miles offshore. Geologists speculate that vast new deposits of tin may be detected still farther out as new methods of prospecting are applied. At present, however, the deposits found in readily-mined underwater locations promise ample supplies of tin for many years to come.

Iron

A few years ago ocean prospectors dredging up samples of earth from the sea floor near

Kyushu, the southernmost island of Japan, announced that they had struck one of the world's greatest deposits of iron. They calculated that lying in shallow water were at least 1,700,000,000 metric tons of magnetite sand. Samples showed it to be almost unbelievably rich in iron. Since then, mining operations over a period of years have proved that the original conclusion was correct. The undersea sand runs as much as 56 per cent iron.

Aragonite

Perhaps sand does not sound like a very valuable sea product, but it joins the list of mineral treasures now being exploited. The kind known as colite aragonite is used in the manufacture of cement, quicklime, glass, rubber, and plastic. With its many applications, aragonite is greatly needed. Recently sea prospectors have found deposits of these sands off the Bahamas in amounts described as "inexhaustible." Engineers report that this find contains as much as 50,000,000,000 tons of this valuable material, which can be easily mined with rather simple dredging equipment.

Phosphorites

In a hungry world where fertilizer is the key to increasing food production, prospectors are eagerly seeking new sources of the phosphorus that goes into fertilizers. The greatest deposits of all are almost certain to lie under the sea, and the most intensively prospected area is off the west coast of the U.S. Here, by 1967, geologists had located more than a hundred promising underwater sites that contain vast quantities of phosphorites. Many of the deposits are in water as shallow as 300 feet deep. Since this mineral comes in layers not much more than 3 feet thick, engineers believe that mining can be accomplished with simple drag dredges.

Sulphur

Sulphur, the golden mineral with hundreds of industrial uses, is found deep below ground. Modern scientific prospectors search for it somewhat as they do for oil, probing the earth with drills to bring up samples from areas where they believe deposits may lie. Today they are carrying out exploratory drilling in many spots on the sea floor.

The searchers are inspired by the success of the pioneering venture in extracting sulphur from the earth beneath the sea. Seven miles off the shore of Louisiana, drillers struck an immense deposit lying 1,800 to 2,500 feet below the sea floor. To mine it, the Freeport Sulphur Company created a man-made island of steel, Grand Isle, on which are living quarters for 150 men. They work the giant pumps and other equipment that bring up the sulphur in liquid form and send it to shore via an underwater pipeline.

An offshore sulphur mine in the Gulf of Mexico. Water heated to 320 degrees F. is injected into sulphur deposits below the gulf floor. This melts the sulphur so it can be brought to the surface in liquid form.

The amazing manganese nodules

When the British oceanographic ship H.M.S. *Challenger* made her great pioneering voyage in the 1879's, among the prizes her scientists brought up from the sea floor were some curious dark lumps of "stone." As the oceanographers studied them, they learned that these odd potato-shaped lumps were really a kind of mineral ore, containing large amounts of manganese and iron. A quarter of a century later, scientists aboard the U.S. Bureau of Fisheries ship *Albatross*, on a similar voyage of exploration, dredged up more of the lumps, which have come to be called "nodules." They were not, the American researchers reported, limited to any one place. The sea floor in many different areas and at many different depths was littered with them.

Where did the nodules, which lay on the sea floor in countless millions, come from? Over the years, scientists pieced together a startling explanation. The nodules *grow*! In the cauldron that is the sea, a chemical reaction involving manganese in sea water takes place. Reacting with dissolved oxygen in the water, the manganese precipitates out as manganese dioxide on any solid object. This object may be a lump of clay, a grain of sand, a shark's tooth, a piece of whale bone, or the skeleton of a dead fish. As more and more of the manganese dioxide forms on this nucleus, it grows larger and larger. "Young" nodules may weigh only a fraction of an

The intricate drilling pattern for a sub-bottom sulphur mine is mapped out with this model.

ounce; mature ones become giant boulders which may weigh tons.

Along with the manganese, particles of iron, cobalt, nickel and copper are also deposited. Some nodules assay about half manganese, 15 per cent iron, with less than 1 per cent of each of the other minerals.

How fast do they grow? Scientists do not

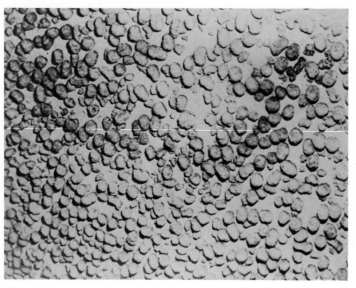

Valuable manganese nodules (these were photographed 11,500 feet down) are constantly accumulating on the sea bed through chemical action.

know for sure. One estimate puts their growth at one millimeter per thousand years. However, their growth could be greater than that. It is believed that in situations where there is more manganese in the water—as there is in parts of the sea near the mouths of certain rivers—the rate of growth may be much greater.

Until recently the existence of the nodules was purely a matter of scientific curiosity— just one of many discoveries made about the sea which seemed to have no practical significance. Then Scripps Institute of Oceanography ships from California began dredging up so many of them from the sea that some scientists asked if it might not be possible to use them as a source of manganese.

The University of California's Institute of Marine Resources, working with the California Department of Mineral Technology, set out to look into this possibility. These and other researches established the fact that there is a belt of nodules some 400 miles off the west coast of both North and South America. Careful studies with underwater cameras have revealed that a 2,000,000-square-mile area is covered with 5 to 7 pounds of nodules per square foot. Nodules have also been

A "key" for unlocking sea-bottom secrets—an ocean bottom corer that extracts a 5-foot-long sample from beneath the ocean floor without disturbing the natural formation. The tube containing the sediment specimen has been removed and is held by the marine geologist on the right.

A cutaway view of manganese nodules shows their onion-like layer structure.

found covering extensive areas in the Atlantic and Indian oceans.

Today, many research organizations are studying ways to claim this sea floor bonanza. Dr. John Mero, one of the world's top authorities on undersea mining, states that "Even if only about 1 per cent of the nodules in the Pacific prove economic to mine, the reserves of many metals in the nodules will still be measured in terms of thousands of years at present rates of free world consumption. Engineering calculations and laboratory experiments indicate that there should be no major problems in adapting existing industrial equipment and processes to mining and processing of manganese nodules."

Engineers propose a number of different nodule mining schemes. At shallow depths, the simplest methods will be to use clamshell or dragline buckets, simply dropping them overside, hauling up loads, and dumping them into the hold of the mining ship.

Another undersea mining tool to use in

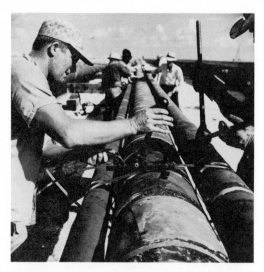

Pipeline through which molten sulphur is sucked up from under the sea.

gathering the nodules may be an undersea tractor. George S. Lockwood, a mining engineer of Global Marine Exploration Company, explains, "It should be practical to build large-scale mining tractors ... equipped with horizontal scanning, high resolution sonar with a range of 500 yards or so, and with television for seeing 50 feet in order to avoid rocks or other sources of interference." Such a tractor would travel about 2 miles an hour, sweeping up nodules in a 20-foot-wide path.

Other experts wonder if the tractor should travel on the ocean floor at all, with all the problems of obstructions and treacherous sand that could cause breakdowns. Instead, why not use a buoyant vehicle that would travel a few feet above the sea floor? It could have a drag that could sweep up the minerals it seeks. Or, as visualized by Dr. Mero, it could be like a floating vacuum cleaner that would suck up the nodules as it passed over them.

Whatever type of undersea mining vehicle turns out to be best, there is still the problem of getting the ore up to the mother ship above. One way is to use buckets into which the mining machine dumps the minerals it gathers. Another is to use a pipeline which sucks up the ore. Engineers are wrestling with the problem of designing such a pipe.

"It is interesting to note," says one expert, "that an 18,000-foot-long, 15-inch-diameter pipeline is about equivalent to a 1/6th-inch diameter drinking straw suspended from a 20-storey building."

The key to successful undersea mining is the mother ship, which must supply power for the underwater operations, working quarters for crew, and storage space for the huge quantities of ore brought up from below. Many shipbuilding firms are at work on designs for new ships and adaptations of old ones.

When the first true undersea mining system starts operation, with whatever combination of methods it uses, experts predict its results will be spectacular. One study indicates that a single ship, working a deposit of manganese nodules, could supply 70 per cent of the needs of the United States, plus, from the same nodules, 35 per cent of its needed cobalt, 25 per cent of its nickel, and 2.8 per cent of its copper.

Aboard the "Cripple Creek," engineers prepare to lower an experimental ocean-floor drilling rig into the sea, using the special hoist in the foreground.

The submersible chamber of the Cachalot diving system. When positioned on the sea floor, it can serve as a base for mineral extraction work conducted by men or machines.

6. DEEP-SEA DRILLING FOR OIL AND KNOWLEDGE

One day in 1966, watchers along the banks of the Mississippi near Vicksburg, saw a towering steel platform walk into the river on giant 133-foot-high legs. The monster, covering almost an acre of river surface, was *Ocean Master II*, the world's largest oil-drilling platform. Once in the river, the monster folded up its legs, and tugs took over. The platform was beginning a long voyage across the Atlantic to help find oil off the coast of Africa.

Undersea oil

Ocean Master II is a triumph of engineering that has come as a climax to a long series of trial-and-error efforts to exploit the deposits of oil that lie under the ocean floor. A global oil rush is under way. Off the shores of every continent a variety of deep-sea drilling platforms are boring deep into the earth beneath the sea to find petroleum and the equally valuable natural gas that surrounds it. Men are at work off the west coast of the U.S.; in the North Sea, off England; in Cook Inlet, Alaska; in the Sulu Sea, off Borneo; in the Sea of Japan; in the Persian Gulf; and in Bass Strait off Australia.

Up to the early 1930's the search for oil stopped at the seashore. Geologists felt certain that there was oil under the sea, but it did not seem possible to drill for it. However, drillers at Eldon, California, made what was considered a bold move. Out into the ocean they built a thousand-foot-long pier. At the end of the pier they put down caissons to hold back the 20-foot-deep water from the drilling site. Above the caissons they erected an ordinary derrick of the type used on shore. By drilling a number of wells, each out at a slant from the platform, they were able to extract oil from a considerably larger area than that protected by the caissons. The experiment worked and other piers were built.

At the same time, on the Gulf Coast in Louisiana, oil men took a different approach. Here, great swampy areas were really part of the sea, for tidal waters flowed into them. The water was not deep—only about 6 feet at high tide—but for a long time the problems of drilling there had baffled the oil men. At last, assured by the geologists that immense deposits of oil were almost certainly located under these tidal marshes, they devised a scheme for drilling in shallow water.

On a huge, flat-bottomed barge they mounted the drilling equipment, and towed the barge to the drilling site. Here they flooded compartments in the barge, causing it to sink to the bottom, where it became solidly

A huge offshore drilling platform. The target-like area is a helicopter landing platform.

The "Christmas tree"—heart of a finished oil well. This complex system of valves controls the flow of crude oil from the well.

anchored. The drilling was done from the part of the barge above the water level.

Encouraged by their experience in drilling in the marshes, the engineers moved drilling rigs out into the open water of the Gulf. At first, when they simply built platforms on ordinary piles, it was not possible to go far from shore. Then they found a way to build platforms in deeper water. The secret was a template, a platform with holes in it. This template-platform was transported to the site and sunk. Then the piles were put down into the holes. The template was then raised, like an elevator, up the piles.

As the engineers boldly made bigger and bigger template-platforms, an ingenious system of transporting them was developed. Instead of being taken piecemeal on construc-

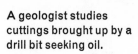

A geologist studies cuttings brought up by a drill bit seeking oil.

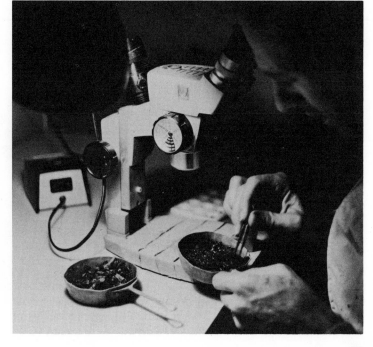

Oil rigs dot the Gulf of Mexico off Louisiana—one of the first offshore oil fields to be exploited.

tion barges, they were placed on buoyancy tanks and floated to the site. It was found that they could be made large enough to house not only the drilling equipment, but living quarters for the crew as well. The tender, a ship that had always had to stand by previously, was no longer needed. A smaller craft could make the trips between platform and shore.

After more experimenting, another improvement was found. Tubular steel legs were substituted for driven piles. As many as 12 of these giant legs were used to support one platform. They were lowered into place at the drilling site, where immense hydraulic jacks raised the platform. These were the "Texas Towers", thus named because the early ones operated off Texas.

These huge platforms opened up many oil fields in the Gulf of Mexico. However, they had one drawback. Once in place they permitted drilling in only a limited area. Often the oil a Texas Tower could extract could not pay for its enormous construction cost, which might run as high as $5,000,000.

The vessel in the background provides living space for the men who work on this oil rig off the Nigerian coast.

What was needed was a movable platform —one that would not be fastened to the sea floor permanently, but, after tapping the oil in one vicinity, could move on. The problems of designing such a tower were formidable, but they did not defeat an engineering genius named Robert Le Tourneau. Famed for his marvelous earth-moving machines used on dry land, Le Tourneau, in the mid-1950's, turned his talents to designing movable sea platforms.

The amazing structures he created can literally "walk" in the water. Triangular, the Le Tourneau platforms have steel "legs" operated by electric motors and gearing systems. After being towed to a drilling site, they have proved their powers by striding into water as deep as 100 feet, where, with their great legs firmly planted in the sea bed, they have provided a secure platform for the oil well drillers.

Such a platform is *Ocean Master II* which, in 1967, began to drill for oil off the shores of Africa. After its 6,000-mile, 2-month-long voyage from the Mississippi River, *Ocean Master II* was put to work on the deepest wells ever tackled up to that time by platforms of this type. It operated in water 300 feet deep.

The statistics describing this 8,500-ton giant are impressive. The rig measures 593 feet from the bottom of its fully extended legs to the top of its derrick—as high as a 60-floor building. (When it walked from the factory where it was built, its legs were only 133 feet high; the rest of the height was fastened on after its sea voyage.) Each huge leg measures 40 feet across. The barge-like hexagonal-shaped hull is 211 feet long and 208 feet across at its widest point. In its acre of space it not only provides room for the heavy equipment and thousands of feet of drill pipe, but also living quarters for the crew of 105 needed to operate this complex of drilling machinery.

Floating platforms

Remarkable as the mighty movable towers on legs may be, they can be used only in comparatively shallow water. While their legs can be made longer and longer, there is a limit on how deep they can go. How can we tap the oil that geologists know exists in vast quantities under thousands of feet of water?

"Why not drill from a floating platform?" a few bold engineers asked. In the early 1950's they were laughed at by their colleagues. How could any platform or ship be made steady enough to withstand the vibrations of the drilling process?

They were hard-hitting, sensible questions, but the lure of undersea oil was enough to convince oil companies that they should at least explore the possibilities of this revolu-

Model of one of the four man-made oil islands located off Long Beach, California. The islands have been landscaped and the derricks enclosed in bright towers, turning what would have been an eyesore into an attractive display.

A multi-level drilling platform in the rich off-shore oil fields below California waters.

The tiny figures of the men demonstrate the large size of an offshore oil platform.

"Roughnecks"—oil men who work on the platform floor—wrestle a 30-foot length of drill pipe into position. A string of such pipes (stacked in background) will drill through thousands of feet of ocean bottom to the oil-bearing strata.

tionary sea venture. *C*ontinental, *U*nion, *S*hell and *S*uperior Oil Companies—known as the CUSS group—joined forces to sponsor the world's first deep-sea drilling ship. Called the *Submarex,* she was a converted U.S. Navy patrol boat. Aboard her was mounted an ordinary rotary drilling rig. The little *Submarex* listed as much as 20 degrees as the drilling apparatus, suspended overside, went into action. But she did not capsize. With the ship held in place by 4 anchors, the oil scientists managed to drill one hole in 1,500 feet of water.

Throughout the oil world, there was much excitement. If a small vessel like the *Submarex* could actually allow drilling in deep water, then bigger ships would certainly be better.

Many floating platforms built since then are made like the mighty *Blue Water*, a pioneering venture of Shell Oil. A 242-foot-long barge, it rests on a series of open grids. When afloat, more than half the structure is beneath the surface. The grid members are hollow, containing ballast tanks. The amount of ballast can be varied, enabling the "captain" of the *Blue Water* to fit its degree of buoyancy to sea conditions. Anchored by eight mooring lines, each secured to a 20,000-pound anchor, the craft pitches and rolls less than 5 degrees when battered by 28-foot waves and lashed by 65-mile-per-hour winds. It remains steady as the pipe whirls

Tugboats tow a giant 1,000-ton drilling rig to a site in the Persian Gulf, where an undersea oil reservoir has been discovered.

down into the hole being drilled thousands of feet below the sea.

The beginning of "drilling to learn"

The richest harvest of undersea drilling may turn out to be not oil and natural gas, but *knowledge*. For under the seas, science has made discoveries that can lead to new understanding of our planet.

The story really began many years ago in the laboratory of a Yugoslavian scientist. One day in October, 1909, Professor Andrija Mohorovičić of the University of Zagreb looked with puzzlement at the wavy lines made by the stylus of the lab seismograph. They indicated a small earthquake at a point calculated as being in Croatia. However, what fascinated him was the fact that the seismograph had recorded a double set of waves. Other scientists, in earthquake laboratories throughout Europe, also noticed the double waves. They concluded simply that there had been two shocks, one larger than the other.

However, this did not satisfy the Zagreb professor. He sent for records made at other seismographic stations to see if he could turn up any clues that might lead to an explanation of this strange difference in speed. He finally concluded that there had been only one shock and that the waves from it had travelled through different kinds of rocks in the earth.

In his report to the world, which came in the form of a paper called "The Great Earthquake of 1909," the scientist depicted

A floating drilling rig searching for oil and gas off the coast of Victoria, Australia.

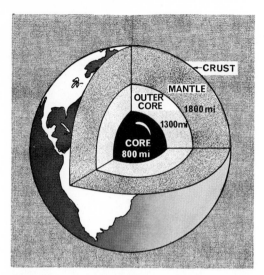

Scientists postulate that the earth is comprised of concentric spheres. The central core is believed to be solid, suspended in a liquid outer core. Surrounding the cores is the 1,800-mile-thick mantle.

layers in the earth—a top one referred to as the *crust*, and one underneath it as the *mantle*. The "slow" waves from the quake had travelled through the crust; the "fast" ones through the mantle. Later, it was established that these layers did indeed exist, and that they were separated by a layer which geologists termed a "seismic discontinuity." This intermediate zone was christened the "Mohorovičić Discontinuity," quite promptly shortened by scientists and laymen alike to "The Moho."

While science has found many ways to determine what's inside the earth, no scientist, until very recently, seriously hoped to see actual samples of anything more than the equivalent of a pin scratch on the earth's surface. Now science is optimistic that we will be able to drill all the way through the earth's crust, into the mysterious underlying Moho. From these deep drillings it is hoped that we can learn much more about the structure and history of the earth through first-hand physical analysis of Moho samples.

The proposed research became a possibility when ocean scientists determined that while the Moho boundary lies 20 to 30 miles under the continents, it is no more than 4 to 9 miles under the ocean floor. Knowing this, Dr. Walter Munk of Scripps Institute of Oceanography, California, and Dr. Harry Hess of Princeton University, made a bold proposal: Why not go to sea to drill a hole to the Moho? A number of other scientists, among them members of the facetiously named American Miscellaneous Society, endorsed the scheme. Many of its members, including the noted geologist, Dr. Willard Bascom, had advised the oil industry in its deep-sea drilling experiments, and they believed that all the technical obstacles in the way of drilling under the sea could be conquered. The National Science Foundation agreed and put up $1,500,000 to start an experimental drilling schedule. The large oil companies joined the effort by contributing equipment, including the drilling barge *CUSS I.*

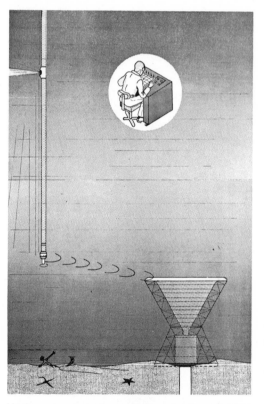

Undersea apparatus which solved a problem described as "like threading a needle on the ground with a fine thread of wire from the top of a 60-floor building." The difficulty was re-entering the hole 15,000 feet under water. The solution: a sonar transponder that enables the drill pipe to home in on the funnel-shaped device at the top of the hole.

Early deep-sea drilling experiments

In March, 1961, the scientists and technicians aboard *CUSS I* succeeded in drilling the first holes in the deep ocean floor. Working in 11,700 feet of water in the Pacific off the West Coast of Mexico, they brought up samples of volcanic rock that had lain undisturbed for more than 30,000,000 years.

After this pioneering effort, other drillings were made. Oddly enough, the final one that gave the most severe test to the drilling equipment was conducted far inland. Scientists had long searched for a suitable place to try out the drills, and they found it on the Leona Valley Ranch, near Uvalde, Texas. Here they had discovered the presence of a large body of hard volcanic rock, with its top only 485 feet beneath the ground. This rock, much like that which they will have to cut through under the sea, extends downwards 3,000 feet. In 1965, after 81 days of test drilling, the engineers announced triumphantly that the trial run was a complete success.

It was proposed to begin drilling at a site 115 miles northeast of the island of Maui in the Hawaiian group. Here science was to stage its biggest venture in learning about our earth, as the massive drills, operating from a mighty drilling barge, were to go down 35,000 feet to reach the Moho.*

Contributions to technology

Long before science was to begin deep drilling operations, the art and science of drilling had to be greatly advanced by new tools and techniques. Every phase of the research called for pioneering in a new realm of instruments which are certain to find other uses in science and the petroleum industry. Up to early 1966, research had produced 103 inventions. Many have already been put to work in offshore drilling for oil. Look at some

*Project Mohole, however, was postponed in 1967, when Congress failed to authorize funds.

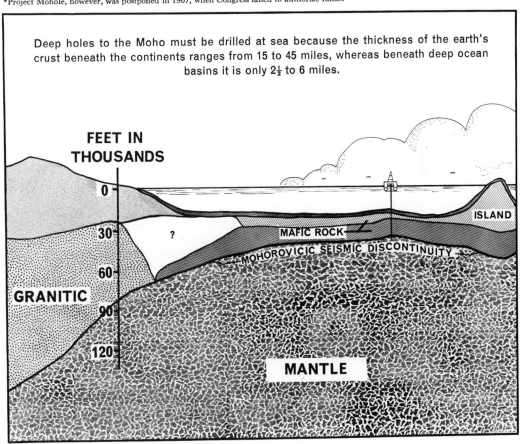

Deep holes to the Moho must be drilled at sea because the thickness of the earth's crust beneath the continents ranges from 15 to 45 miles, whereas beneath deep ocean basins it is only 2½ to 6 miles.

FEET IN THOUSANDS

0
30
60
90
120

GRANITIC

?

ISLAND

MAFIC ROCK

MOHOROVICIC SEISMIC DISCONTINUITY

MANTLE

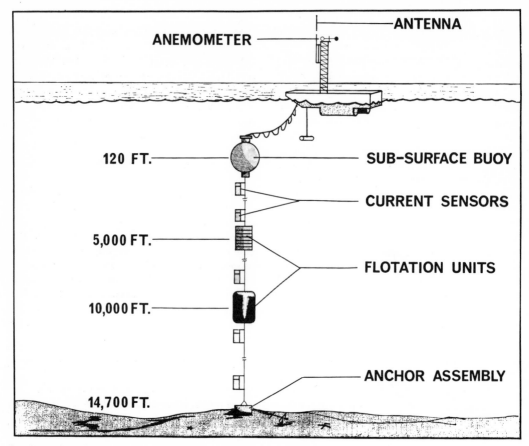

ANEMOMETER ── | ── ANTENNA

120 FT. ──────────── SUB-SURFACE BUOY

──────── CURRENT SENSORS

5,000 FT. ────────

──────── FLOTATION UNITS

10,000 FT. ────────

──────── ANCHOR ASSEMBLY

14,700 FT.

Implanted in the sea near the drilling platform, this complex string of instruments will measure such phenomena as the direction and velocity of currents.

of the major contributions made and proposed:

DRILLING PLATFORM: This gigantic structure, with its $1\frac{1}{2}$-acre operating deck will rest on twin submarine hulls. Large as it will be, its powerful 15,000-h.p. engines will move it through the water at a speed of 10 knots. The great contribution of its design is not its size or mobility, however, but its stability. It is designed to be the most stable drilling platform ever made. Computer calculations and tests made with models indicate that it "will not roll more than 4 degrees or heave

New tools developed were tested at this well in Texas by drilling through basaltic rock with a compressive strength of 58,000-pounds psi—only slightly less than that of ordinary steel.

Model of the proposed giant drilling platform. The twin submarine pontoons which provide the craft's buoyancy are 390 feet long.

more than $3\frac{1}{2}$ feet while maintaining a fixed position within a 400-foot radius circle while subjected to a 3-knot current, 30-knot winds and 25-foot waves."

THE POSITIONING SYSTEM: This remarkable system will keep the platform on station in water too deep for ordinary anchorage. Three separate sonar systems will team with twin computers to keep track of the lateral distance of the platform from the vertical axis of the hole being drilled. If the distance should go beyond pre-determined limits, computers will order the six, 1,000-horsepower electrically operated positioning units to move the platform back into the correct position.

THE CASING SYSTEM: An intricate system of pipes, buoys, and connecting mechanisms, called the casing, or riser, system, has been designed to extend from the drilling vessel to the sea floor base. One of the developments that have made it possible is a new lightweight buoyant material known as syntactif foam. It has properties which will make it useful in many other kinds of undersea apparatus.

A turbocorer, a new, powerful undersea drill, hanging in a derrick.

SONAR RE-ENTRY SYSTEM: A system of sonar devices causes drilling apparatus to "home in" on the exact location of the proposed hole. Powerful jet nozzles move the drilling apparatus to the position the sonar apparatus indicates is correct.

THE TURBO-CORER: A device eliminates the need to rotate the long string of drill pipe in order to turn the bit. It is powered by high-pressure drilling fluid surging through the turbine mounted in the tool. This turns the bit at speeds of up to 600 rpm.

The instruments developed for use with the turbo-corer are a remarkable advance in themselves. For the first time many bottom-hole operations are accurately and instantaneously indicated on surface instruments, giving the operators above an accurate knowledge of just what is happening in the drilling operation.

THE ELECTRO-CORER: This is a device similar to the turbo-corer, but designed to operate at slower speeds.

SIDE-WALL CORING TOOL: This ingenious tool is sent down to the depth from which cores are desired. Pads extend against the side of the hole to anchor the tool in place, and then twin saws bite into the sides of the hole. As a triangular wedge is cut from the rock, it breaks into 8-inch lengths and falls into a basket inside the tool. This gives geologists a unique means of getting earth samples from any desired depth as the hole goes down.

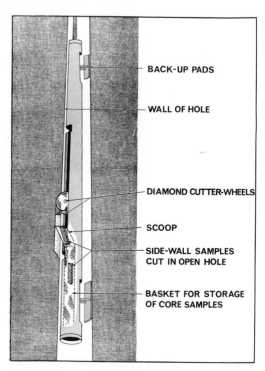

A side-wall coring tool, developed as a by-product of research. It permits taking core samples at any depth as the drill descends.

7. SEA-WATER WEALTH

A ship moved swiftly across the waters of the English Channel. In its wake, attached to a cable, a metal framework held a number of strips of glass fabric. This odd tow was not an oceanographic instrument or a net to catch fish. The scientists who were conducting the experiment had quite a different catch in mind.

Later came the announcement from Dr. Robert Spence of England's Atomic Energy Research Centre at Harwell. The scientists had indeed caught something. The sheets of glass fabric had come back from their voyage saturated with uranium. Titanium hydroxide, the chemical with which they were treated, had, as the researchers had hoped it would, created a chemical reaction which separated the uranyl ions from sea water, and caused them to collect on the towed fabric.

Science had taken a big step forward in the old dream of extracting mineral riches from sea water. To be sure, as Dr. Spence pointed out, this method of uranium recovery would cost four times as much as present methods and would not be immediately practical. However, in a world that is going to need all the uranium it can find, the process, with technological improvements, might be made to pay out in the not too distant future. Likely spots in the sea where there is movement of sea water could provide inexhaustible supplies for fixed or floating uranium-extraction plants. At one such spot alone, Key West, Florida, where the Florida current sweeps north out of the Gulf of Mexico, Dr. Spence estimated that 2,000,000 tons of uranium are carried past each year.

Sea-water riches

The mineral wealth in sea water has been known for a long time. Though sea water is 96.5 per cent pure water, it contains an astonishing number and quantity of other substances.

In order of their abundance, here are some of the elements sea water contains:

Chlorine	Copper
Sodium	Zinc
Magnesium	Lead
Sulphur	Selenium
Calcium	Cesium
Potassium	Uranium
Bromine	Molybdenum
Carbon	Thorium
Strontium	Cerium
Boron	Silver
Silicon	Vanadium
Fluorine	Lanthanum
Nitrogen	Yttrium
Aluminum	Nickel
Rubidium	Scandium
Lithium	Mercury
Phosphorus	Gold
Barium	Radium
Iodine	Cadmium
Arsenic	Chromium
Iron	Cobalt
Manganese	Tin

Even though sea water contains these elements in minute amounts, there is so much of it that the total quantities of minerals in the sea are staggering. The amount of dissolved substances in 300,000,000 cubic miles of the World Ocean is calculated to include 20,000,000,000 tons of uranium; 15,000,000,000 tons of copper; 15,000,000,000 tons of manganese; 500,000,000 tons of silver, and 10,000,000 tons of gold.

Salt from the sea

It is estimated that there are about 50,000,000,000,000 tons of salt dissolved in the sea. If this amount were spread out, dry,

Several Nansen bottles, attached in series to a cable, will collect sea water samples at specific depths when actuated by sliding weights.

it would cover every foot of land surface of our globe to a depth of 502 feet.

With such salt abundance, it was natural that man's first success in getting mineral riches from the sea came in the extraction of salt. This is no minor matter, as salt is a chemical of vast importance to modern industry. Only 5 per cent of it is produced for table use. The other 95 per cent goes into the making of more than 14,000 different products. Metals, paper, plastics, and textiles are just a few of the industrial materials which require salt at some stage of manufacture.

Getting salt from the sea is basically a matter of letting the water evaporate, but that is not quite so simple as it sounds. The modern scientific procedures can best be seen by visiting the largest U.S. sea-salt "factories," on the shores of San Francisco Bay.

The process starts with letting sea water into huge shallow ponds, each covering hundreds of acres. Amazingly, it will take 6 years from the time the water carries in its cargo of salt until the time that salt is ready to head for your table or for the factories where it performs so many tasks. From the big ponds, the sea water flows to smaller concentration ponds. As the water evaporates, the percentage of salinity increases. Technicians take frequent hydrometer readings of the brine, and when it reaches a certain concentration, they pump it into another large pond. Here the minerals in the now greatly

concentrated brine fall to the bottom of the pond. The substance which drops out in the greatest quantity is calcium phosphate, commonly called lime. The brine, minus its lime and other constituents, is moved on to a harvesting pond, where it deposits what is by now 99 per cent pure salt in layers about 6 inches thick. This salt is then scooped up by giant machines and carried to a factory where it is washed to remove the few impurities left.

Magnesium from the sea

One cubic mile of sea water contains about 6,000,000 tons of magnesium—enough to make a bar one foot in diameter and 20,000 miles long. It is the first mineral, other than salt, that man has succeeded in extracting from the sea in any quantity.

It is fortunate that by its success in getting magnesium from sea water, science has assured the world of an unlimited supply of this mineral. Magnesium has become increasingly important in many industries and in our daily lives. This light metal (steel is $4\frac{1}{2}$ times heavier than magnesium) has a host of structural and non-structural uses. Alloyed with aluminum, zinc and various other minerals, it is used in hundreds of parts in rockets, aircraft, electronic equipment and in many kinds of machines. Its special electrical properties give it many uses in protecting ships, pipelines and home water heaters from corrosion. Its light weight gives it a place in

OYSTER SHELLS
BURNED TO LIME
PRECIPITATED | Mg HYDRATE
OCEAN WATER

CONVERTED TO Mg CHLORIDE BY ADDITION OF HYDROCHLORIC ACID

FILTERS

DRIERS

ELECTROLYTIC CELLS

CHLORINE GAS RETURNED TO PROCESS AS HYDROCHLORIC ACID

MAGNESIUM INGOTS

(Above) Oyster shells dredged from the sea bottom. The shells are burned into lime and are an important ingredient in the process which extracts magnesium from sea water.

← The chemical process by which magnesium is obtained from sea water.

hundreds of products, ranging from skis to power tools.

Magnesium, after salt, was the first major mineral to be taken from the ocean because engineers discovered that a fairly simple series of chemical and electrical steps can make sea water give up the 0.13 per cent of the magnesium it contains. Dow Chemical Company chemists perfected the process far from the sea, using water from the brine wells of Michigan, which also yielded many other chemical products.

Today Dow's giant plant on the of Gulf Mexico processes 600,000 gallons of water a minute. The process begins when sea water is pumped into settling tanks and mixed with lime. Lime contains calcium that replaces magnesium in the sea water and the insoluble magnesium hydroxide that results from this reaction settles out of the water. It is then withdrawn from the bottom of the tanks and processed in huge filters. Hydrochloric acid prepared from natural gas and chlorine is used to treat the magnesium

Millions of gallons of sea water are pumped daily through these intakes at a magnesium extracting plant on the Texas coast.

hydroxide, producing magnesium chloride, which is then evaporated to a dry powder.

This powder, called "cell feed," is fed into electrolytic cells, where electricity converts it to magnesium and chlorine gas. The magnesium is at last ready to be converted into ingots and pigs, which will in turn go into the host of products that use this light metal from the sea.

Ingeniously, the Dow engineers have made the sea give up one of the chemicals used in the extraction process. Oyster shells dredged from the sea floor, and roasted, provide large quantities of lime. There is also a bonus in the form of chlorine gas which emerges with magnesium in the final stage of the process. It returns to the cycle as hydrochloric acid.

The 70,000 tons of magnesium extracted from the sea each year may be only a small sample of the mineral bounty sea water may one day yield. But it is important as an indication of what the future may hold. Willard Dow, a chemist with many scientific achievements to his credit, was always proudest of the success of his company's seafaring venture. "Chemical ingenuity, combined with God's gift of the Sea, will give man inexhaustible mineral riches," he predicted.

Gold from sea water

In 1965, Dr. Ernest Bayer, a scientist at Tübingen University, Germany, announced that he had succeeded in extracting gold from sea water. He used a process in which the sea water, mixed with other chemicals, was shaken for 12 hours. After that the chemicals were filtered out, and what was left was a tiny quantity of gold. Dr. Bayer's experiment was conducted on a small scale, using 100 litres of sea water, and the amount of gold produced was really minute—only 1.4 micrograms. Nonetheless, this German chemist moved closer than anyone before towards realizing the old dream of getting gold from sea water.

It is a dream that has tantalized many eminent scientists since the noted Svante Arrenhius, of Sweden, made an announcement in 1902. He had, he stated, analyzed sea water brought back by an oceanographic expedition and found that it contained a surprising amount of gold—about 0.06 of an ounce per ton of sea water. For a long time this figure was accepted, and it excited the interest of another Nobel Prize winning scientist, Fritz Haber, a brilliant German chemist. In the years after World War I, Haber became obsessed with the idea that his country's huge war debt could be paid off by gold extracted from the sea. He believed that he could find a chemical method of making gold precipitate from sea water. He also believed that somewhere in the oceans of the world there must be currents of water which contained more gold than water elsewhere. He spoke of "veins" of gold in the sea.

To locate these currents, the German research ship, *Meteor*, set out in 1925 on what was popularly labelled a "gold-hunting expedition." Actually, the scientists aboard the *Meteor* did much investigating of other ocean phenomena as, for 777 days, they crisscrossed the Atlantic, making a series of closely-spaced observations in the South Atlantic.

When the *Meteor* finally came back to home port, Haber hurried to his laboratory with the hundreds of sea water samples the scientists had brought him. He emerged a shaken man. Far from being richer in gold, the water assayed only a tiny fraction of the amount Arrenhius had said sea water contained. What was wrong?

The dismayed Haber got in touch with Arrenhius, to ask a question he had not checked on before. What kind of bottles had the Swedish oceanographers used for their sea water samples?

"Metal," said Arrenhius.

There was the disturbing answer. Arrenhius had made a wild error in his calculations. The metal in the bottles had in itself contained a minute amount of gold. It had dissolved in the sea water and upset the results of his analysis. The water gathered by *Meteor* researchers was collected in glass bottles, so that Haber's analysis was the correct one. Sea water contained only a thousandth as much gold as he had believed.

After this upsetting information was re-

A huge electrolytic cell used in the final stage of extracting magnesium from sea water. The cell converts magnesium chloride into primary magnesium and chlorine gas.

vealed, other scientists still pursued the dream of gold from ocean water. One of them was Dr. Georges Claude, a French scientist. Any night in any city in the world you can see one of his discoveries, for he is noted as the developer of neon lights. Claude conceived the idea that he could develop a chemical filter which, towed behind a ship, would collect gold. He actually constructed such a filter and towed it behind his ship, the *San Jose*, off the Pacific Coast of the U.S. His gold collector, unfortunately, collected no gold.

The first successful extraction of gold from sea water must be credited to Willard Dow and the engineers of Dow Chemical who succeeded so magnificently in making ocean water give up its magnesium. In the mid-1930's, they applied Haber's chemical methods to some of the tremendous flow of water pouring through tanks in experiments with bromine extraction. From 12 metric tons of sea water they actually did produce a tiny amount of gold. It weighed only 0.09 milligrams, but it *was* gold.

Today's scientists do not scoff at the efforts of pioneers like Dr. Haber who dreamed of getting gold from sea water. The gold is there; it can be extracted. It seems only a matter of time until someone finds a way to cut the cost of tapping the enormous treasure trove of this precious mineral waiting in the World Ocean.

Sea water's greatest treasure

The greatest treasure in sea water may be water!

We live in a world that is increasingly short of water. In the U.S. headlines proclaim grim news of drinking water shortages as reservoirs dry up, water tables drop, and once adequate sources of supply fail to meet burgeoning needs. In other parts of the world, industry and agriculture are stunted by lack of water.

Under primitive conditions, a mere 5 gallons of water a day per person was a generous supply. In many areas today people are still getting along on no more water than that. Yet in modern cities, almost 200 gallons a day per capita may be required. It takes 25 gallons for a five-minute shower, for instance.

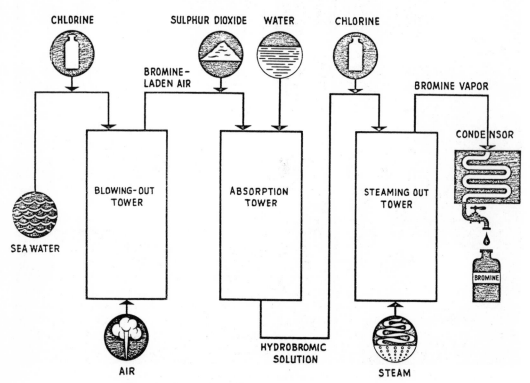

Bromine is produced from sea water by this process.

An earthquake-caused tidal wave cut off the water supply to the town of Point Barrow, Alaska and the nearby Air Force base. These two portable desalination plants were flown in and in a few hours were producing fresh water at the rate of 40,000 gallons a day.

Industry gulps down huge quantities of water. It takes 240,000 gallons to produce one ton of acetate for use in plastics. It takes 660,000 gallons to make a ton of synthetic rubber. Agriculture, too, needs staggering amounts of water. Scientists calculate that it takes, in one way and another, more than 800 gallons of water to make a loaf of bread; 3,750 gallons to produce one pound of beef.

Altogether, the United States alone needs 390,000,000,000 gallons of fresh water a day and its water use is increasing at the rate of 25,000 gallons a *minute*!

The big and frightening question facing the world is: Where is the water to come from? To find out, world scientists have united in a concerted effort called the International Hydrological Decade, which was inaugurated on January 1, 1965. For a 10-year period, thousands of scientists will be devoting themselves to exploring all aspects of water resources and man's needs. Individual countries have special organizations of their own devoted to the problem; in the U.S., it is the Federal Resources Council.

Desalting sea water

While science is finding many ways to provide more water for a thirsty world—deeper wells, huge water diversion projects, an end to the pollution of great rivers—experts are agreed that these will only help, not solve, the problem. To meet our needs we will have to turn to the 324,000,000 cubic miles of water in the World Ocean, and find a way to take the salt out of sea water.

In different parts of the world, hundreds of desalting experiments are under way. Actually, science has succeeded in finding an almost bewildering variety of methods, some of them very complex. However, they all fall into just two broad classifications. The first calls for taking the water away and leaving the salts and minerals behind. This method includes such processes as distillation, freeze separation and reverse osmosis. The other manner of going at the problem removes the salts and leaves the fresh water behind. The most important process in this category is electrodialysis.

Seven plants at the U.S. Office of Saline Water Research Center, Wrightsville Beach, North Carolina, test different methods of desalination.

Let us look at some of the major processes which are well out of the laboratory stage, and in some cases actually producing quantities of fresh water.

Distillation

The distillation process sounds almost ridiculously simple when it is described in general terms. It consists of applying heat to boil the water and then condensing the vapor as pure water. If you boiled a pan full of salt water, and then collected the drops of water that condensed on the cover of the pan, you would be carrying out this basic process. Indeed, this is a fact known to man throughout history.

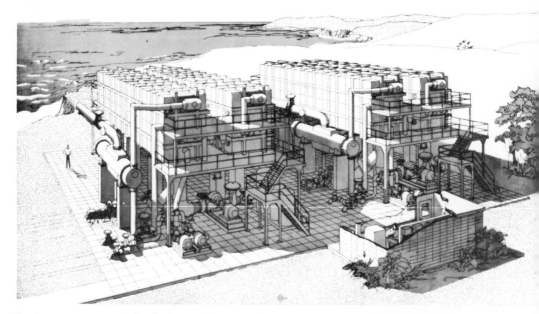

The largest sea water distillation plant on the European continent—the 1,200,000 gallon-per-day unit at Taranto, Italy. The water from this plant is the purest ever produced on a large scale—one part salt per million parts water.

A proposed dual-purpose nuclear power and desalination plant on a 40-acre man-made island half a mile off the California coast.

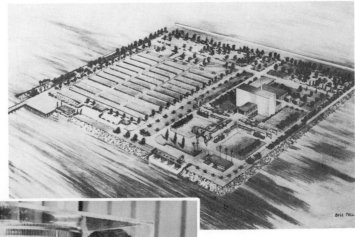

An engineer checks the operation of a 100-gallon-a-day desalination unit.

A huge 800,000 gallon-per-day flash evaporator-type desalination unit recently installed on the island of Aruba in the Netherlands West Indies.

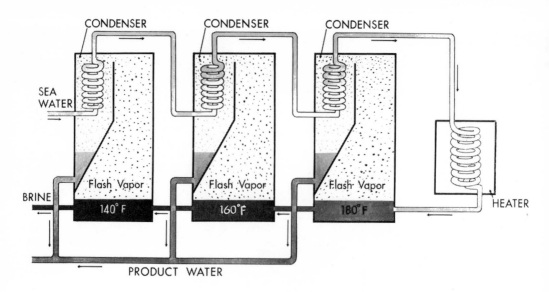

Diagram of the flash distillation process.

"When sea water evaporates it becomes fresh and the condensation from its steam is not salt," said Aristotle.

Today science has developed ways of overcoming the worst drawback of this old, simple form of desalting water—its wasteful use of heat. One important method now being used in large plants is *multi-stage flash distillation*. (See diagram.) In this process, sea water is heated and then introduced into a large chamber where a pressure just below the boiling point of the hot brine is maintained. When the brine enters this chamber, the reduced pressure causes part of the liquid to boil immediately—or flash—into steam. The remaining brine is passed through a series of similar chambers at successively higher vacuums where the flash process is repeated at progressively higher temperatures. Progressive heating is accomplished by piping the incoming sea water through the flash chambers, starting at the low temperature end. In each chamber, the flashed vapor condenses as it gives up its heat to the cooler sea water in the condenser. By this arrangement, about 90 per cent of the heat required for boiling is recirculated and only 10 per cent is supplied by the salt water heater.

Another type of distillation process is *long tube vertical distillation*, the method used in a pioneer million-gallon-a-day plant at Free-port, Texas, set up for demonstration purposes by the U.S. Office of Saline Water. (See diagram.) It works this way:

Steam is admitted into the first evaporator, filling the space around the tube bundle and causing part of the sea water to boil as it falls through the tubes. A mixture of vapor and hot brine emerges at the bottom. The hot brine is pumped to the top of the second evaporator, where, under slightly reduced pressure, it again falls through the tubes. Vapor produced in the first effect flows to the outside of the tube bundle in the second effect. Here the vapor is condensed to fresh water by giving up its latent heat of vaporization to the sea water falling through the tubes. This again causes part of the water in the tubes to boil. The same process is repeated through all 12 evaporators in the plant.

Vacuum freezing

Scientists are working hard to perfect processes that call for freezing rather than heating sea water to separate it from its salt. It takes less energy to freeze sea water than it does to evaporate it, and researchers are hopeful that they can use it for much larger plants than the experimental 100,000-gallon-per-day plant operated by the Office of Saline Water at Wrightsville Beach, North Carolina.

The process is based on the fact that when

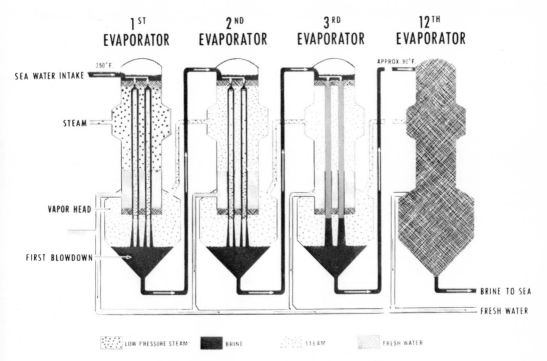

1ST EVAPORATOR   **2ND EVAPORATOR**   **3RD EVAPORATOR**   **12TH EVAPORATOR**

Diagram of the long tube vertical distillation process.

salt water freezes, the brine drops out during the freezing—a fact long observed by Arctic explorers who discovered that, while they could not drink sea water, they could melt sea ice to get fresh water. In experimental freezing systems, the sea water enters the system at 60 to 75 degrees F., passes through a device that removes air, then through heat

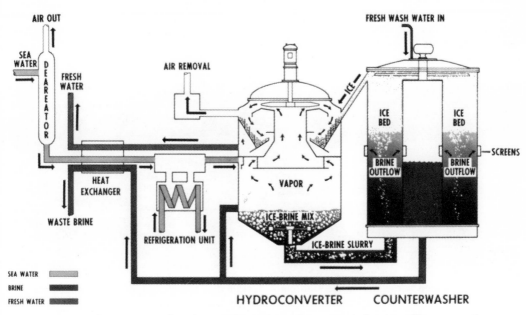

Diagram of the vacuum freezing vapor compression process for de-salting sea water.

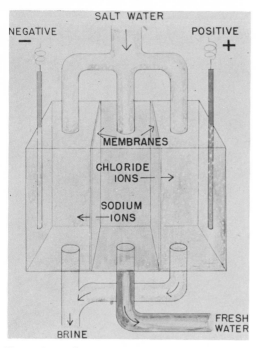

Flow chart of an electrodialysis unit used in de-salting water.

pumped from the freezer to a counter-washer where brine is separated and ice crystals are washed free of salt. From the counter-washer, ice is scraped into a melter. (See diagram.)

Electrodialysis

This method of getting the salt out of water takes advantage of the fact that salts, when dissolved, take the form of positively charged ions called "cations" and negatively charged ions called "anions." The electrodialysis equipment consists of a sandwich of alternating cation- and anion-permeable membranes. Upon the application of an electric current, positively charged ions, such as sodium, pass through the cation-permeable membranes. The negatively charged ions, of which chloride is one, move in the opposite direction and pass through the anion-permeable membranes. The water in the middle of each sandwich is thus depleted of salt, while water accumulating on the outside of the membranes is enriched in it. The membranes are usually sheet plastic material in which the ion-exchange substances have been embedded.

Electrodialysis, at its present stage of development, seems best fitted for desalting water from brackish wells. Further experiments may make it suitable for use on sea water if the problem of high cost can be solved.

exchangers, where it is cooled—partly by recirculated waste brine. This chilled water is then introduced into a freezing chamber where it is converted into a slurry, or thin mixture of liquid water and ice particles. Sea water freezes at 27 degrees F. The slurry is

A nuclear-powered sea-water conversion plant designed at the Oak Ridge National Laboratory. The plant would produce 1,000,000,000 gallons of fresh water a day and enough electrical power for a city of 5,000,000 people.

94

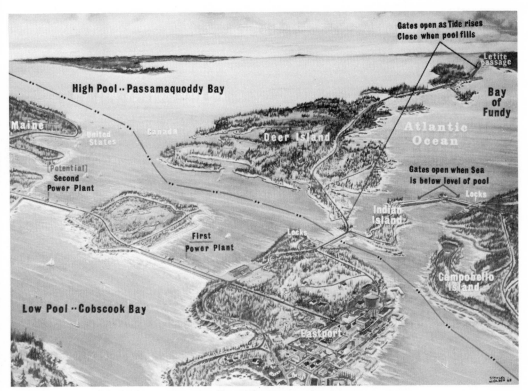

Location of the proposed Passamaquoddy tidal power plant.

8. POWER FROM THE SEA

The lights of Paris looked no different on a late summer night in 1966, but there *was* something different. Some of the electricity that lit the city came from a source that had never produced electricity before—the sea. The energy of the moon operating the tides was at last being put to work for man.

Across the half-mile-wide tidal waters of the Rance River estuary in Brittany, near the spot where the Allies made their landing on the Continent in 1944, stretches a long, low dam. Deep inside it are the ingeniously compact turbines that turn the tide into electricity. To be sure, it was but a single turbine that fed a mere token amount of power—6,000 kilowatts—into the French power grid on that historic day in August, 1966. However, it was proof enough that an engineering triumph was being achieved. Nothing more

stood in the way of full operation of the 24 mighty turbines that, in 1967, would send 240,000 kilowatts of power surging into the Paris transmission lines . . .

The idea of harnessing the tides is not new. Engineers had often speculated on ways to make the restless surge of the tides produce power. In the days before electricity, they worked out many schemes for tidal water wheels, and, indeed, in a few places in Europe small tidal mills were actually built. However, the trouble with tide-operated mills was that the flow of waters provided power for only a short time each day. This same problem confronted engineers in the age of electricity. Calculations always showed that even though baffling engineering difficulties could be overcome, the cost of building a part-time power plant would be prohibitive.

95

An aerial view showing construction work on the giant tidal power plant on France's River Rance.

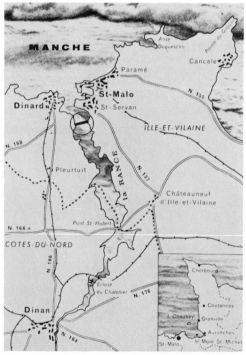

Map showing location of the tidal power plant of the River Rance.

The Passamaquoddy plan

In 1919, an American engineer, Dexter Cooper, began a study of one of the world's most promising locations for a tidal power plant. At Passamaquoddy Bay, an arm of the Bay of Fundy, which separates the state of Maine and the Canadian province of Nova Scotia, the tides are the highest in the world. Sometimes the difference between low tide and high tide is as much as 50 feet. Twice each day the tides send a mighty torrent of water pouring into and out of Passamaquoddy Bay with awesome force.

Cooper drew up plans for a system of dams and power plants in the Bay. At first no one would listen to him. Apart from the vast expense of building such a system, what use would the power be in such a remote spot? Later, as long distance transmission of electricity became feasible, this objection was overcome. So through the years, Cooper kept on urging construction of the "Quoddy" project. Finally he began to get listeners.

Among them was President Franklin D. Roosevelt, who had often vacationed at Campobello Island near Passamaquoddy. He became an enthusiastic backer of Cooper's project, and, even though many engineers

One of the giant bulb turbines of the River Rance tidal power plant, shown during installation.

and economic experts had their doubts about tidal power, the U.S. Congress, at F.D.R.'s urging, appropriated enough money to permit a start on the project. But a combination of engineering and political objections brought it to a halt in 1939.

Talk of Quoddy was revived in the 1960's. John F. Kennedy, another U.S. President who believed in the project, stated, "I think this can be one of the most astonishing and beneficial joint projects that the people of the U.S. have ever undertaken." Canadian and U.S. studies indicated that, although it would cost $1,000,000,000 to build the mighty system of dams, it was technically possible. By the time that North American engineers had something to go on, the French were actually constructing the world's first tidal power plant.

An engineer's dream

More than two centuries ago a French military engineer, Bernard Forest de Belidor, suggested that the tides in the estuary of the Rance River could be harnessed. Of course, in that year of 1737, he knew nothing of generating electricity. His thought was that more efficient and powerful water wheels could be designed. Nothing came of his scheme, though it was talked of from time to time. In the 20th century various engineers spoke of the Rance River tides as a source of electricity, but the problems seemed too formidable and various plans gathered dust in the archives of government ministries.

It was 1940 when Robert Gibrat, a brilliant electrical engineer, chanced upon drawings of one of these schemes, made up by a forgotten designer. As director of Electricity Distribution for France's Ministry of Public Works, Gibrat had long been fascinated by the tides. He had grown up on the rugged coast of Brittany, where, as a boy, he had watched the tides thundering in. Now, in his office in war-torn France, he studied with eager in-

An alternator, part of the generating equipment in the River Rance tidal power plant.

The Rance dam under construction.

terest the old Rance River plans along with Cooper's plan for Passamaquoddy. He could see that they had some flaws, yet couldn't modern engineers, with all their skills and knowledge, manage to devise a workable way of harnessing at least some tidal power that was going to waste?

Gibrat resolved to devote his life to making the old River Rance dream a reality. Not much could be done during the war, but Gibrat began to form plans for a power plant in the estuary, where, when the tide comes in, 280,000,000 gallons of water a minute churn into a narrow passageway. Consulting with other engineers, Gibrat found many who were glad to work with him in making drawings and calculations.

When the war ended, Gibrat and his group were ready. They believed they had found the answers to problems that had plagued earlier engineers. If they could just get financial backing, they were sure that they could give France a great new source of power. Eventually, they did get the money, first from a private firm, then from the French Government. By 1959 they had constructed a working miniature tidal plant, which, built exactly to scale, duplicated all the conditions they would face in building the full-sized structure. By 1961, actual construction began, and five years later came that first historic moment when electricity generated by the sea flowed into the national power grid.

98

How the tides produce power

Just how can the tides produce power? The principles involved are not difficult to understand. Let Jacques Duport, Chief Engineer of the French *Société Grenobloise d'Etudes et d'Applications Hydrauliques* (SOGREAH) explain:

"Let us take an estuary and close it in with a sluice dam, thus creating a basin. When the tide rises, the sluices are opened, and the water rushes into the basin. At high tide, the

The power of the tides is illustrated by these violent back-flowing currents on the downstream side of the Rance Tidal Power Plant.

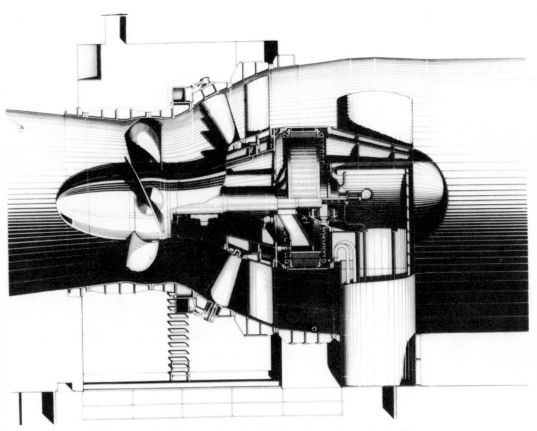

The bulb turbine which makes it possible to harness the tides.

sluice gates are closed again and the ebbing water gives rise to a head—a comparatively small one, to be sure—between the estuary level and that of water in the basin.

"If we have installed a mill-wheel or even a turbine in the dam, we have only to open the distributing valve to empty the basin and thus retrieve energy from the tidal water. It was in this way that the tidal mill-wheels in the creeks and bays of the Breton coast used to operate. This method of working is the simplest imaginable . . . Energy is produced when the basin is emptied into the sea . . ."

This basic idea for producing tidal power, is, as Jacques Duport states, "the simplest imaginable." To build power plants to use the tides more efficiently, engineers had to find ways to make the water do more work. When it is simply allowed to tumble out of the pond in which it has been trapped, it does not produce power over a very long period of time. Accordingly, engineers in France and elsewhere have devoted their attention to using the water as it flows in, as well as out. They have also devised systems of pumps that can increase and prolong the flow of water. Different methods have been developed, but at the great dam on the Rance, the problem was solved in a way no one had ever thought of before.

The wonderful bulb turbine

The device that is the heart of the Rance tidal power plant is a radically new kind of turbine which took the engineers of SOGREAH 20 years to develop. Housed in a watertight bulb 50 feet long and 16 feet in diameter (from the outside it looks very much like a small submarine), this versatile piece of machinery is cunningly designed to perform the work of four separate machines. It serves as:

1. A turbine, operated by water flowing in either direction, without causing the blades to change their direction.

2. A motor. When electricity is fed to the

Location of the tidal power plant in Kislaya inlet, U.S.S.R.

bulb's generating unit instead of being drawn from it, it becomes a powerful electric motor.

3. A pump. The electric motor operates the turbine as a pump.

4. A gate, regulating the flow of water in either direction.

Thus in a single, relatively compact unit, engineers have been able to solve the problems arising from the changing demands of a tidal power system.

Twenty-four of these turbines are housed in a power plant inside the immense 3,000-foot dam that extends across the estuary. The power plant itself does not look much like ordinary hydro-electric installations, with their lines of whirling dynamos. In the Rance dam, the submarine-shaped turbine units are all housed in a tunnel-like structure beneath the floor of the plant. When a turbine requires servicing, workers wearing diving equipment enter through a hatch and descend a ladder into the unit.

The U.S.S.R.'s pilot plant

Scientists of the Soviet Union have shown a particular interest in such projects because Russia contains almost a quarter of the world's

tidal power possibilities. As their first venture in getting water moved by the moon to generate power, Soviet engineers decided to turn the Kola Peninsula, near Finland, into a spacious laboratory to test the possibilities.

As the site of their first dam they chose the Bay of Kislaya on the Peninsula. Here there is a narrow slit between hundred-foot-high cliffs. During the rising tide the water rushes into the Bay at a speed of 13 feet per second. Into this gap the Soviet engineers, directed by Lev Berhnstein, a pioneer advocate of tidal power, moved a pre-fabricated concrete dam. Brought to the scene in two mammoth parts, it is in itself a pioneering venture in dam building. Assembling the concrete slabs and sections of the dam in drydocks and towing them to the site was a fast way to get the power plant built. And, in an Arctic climate where the construction season is short, the whole process of dam building had to be speeded up.

The Kislaya dam uses turbines modelled after the French devices and, in fact, they were constructed by the French firm which built the River Rance turbines.

The U.S.S.R. has announced plans for a

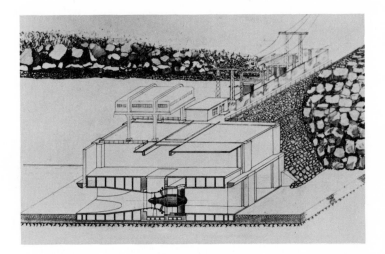

Diagram of the U.S.S.R.'s tidal power plant on the Barents Sea.

huge system of tidal dams on the White Sea, where, in many estuaries, the tides could be harnessed.

Other tides to harness

The success of the French and Russian projects has sparked interest in harnessing tides in other parts of the world.

In England, serious consideration has been given to building a power plant in the estuary of the Severn River, with its 45-foot

tides. Engineers visualize co-operation with France if this plant were built. The difference in tidal patterns on the English side of the Channel would make it a perfect complement to the French project on the Rance. With differing times of maximum power production and national consumption, the French could feed power into the English power grid, and vice versa.

Gibrat, the genius of the French project, has worked up a list of 90 different sites in

A scale model showing installation of a bulb turbine in the U.S.S.R.'s Kislaya Inlet tidal power plant.

Parts of the Kislaya power plant reached this tidal installation by sea. Pre-fabricated units of the dam were towed into position.

other parts of the world where he believes tidal power plants could work. Most prominent, of course, is the Bay of Fundy, which, in his opinion, could become the mightiest tidal power plant in the world, dwarfing the big one on the Rance. Other promising sites are indicated in northern Australia, South Korea, Argentina, and between the United States and Mexico in the Gulf of California.

Power from sea water

Harnessing the tides is not the only way to make the sea yield power. Engineers have found a way to exploit the difference between the temperature of water at the surface and that of the water far below.

Again this is a field in which French engineers have pioneered. At Abidjan, on Africa's Ivory Coast, they have completed an experimental plant that may point the way for much bigger ones. It works this way:

Surface water, which at Abidjan has a temperature of about 82 degrees F., is run through a boiler, where it creates steam. What makes it boil and create steam at a mere 82 degrees? The answer is that above the water in the boiler, a vacuum is created. It is a fact of elementary heat physics that this lowers the temperature at which the water boils. The steam thus created drives a turbine which generates power.

Next the residue of the steam is cooled by 46-degree sea water which has been pumped up from a depth of half a mile. Contact with

the cool water causes the steam to condense. In doing so, by another process of elementary physics, it creates a vacuum, which in turn draws more steam from the 82-degree water through the turbine.

The African plant is not as efficient as engineers believe such plants can be made. New designs have been worked out which do not require pumping the sea water to make use of temperature differences. One engineer has proposed a floating power plant which uses propane gas in pipes as a heat exchange medium to transmit the chilling effect.

It probably will take many years of experimentation but the rewards will be tremendous. Experts calculate that success with temperature differences will give mankind an unlimited source of power. One estimate indicates that it could provide continuous energy 200 times as great as the highest estimate of the world's power needs in the year 2000.

The sea may have still other power potentials. For example, when fresh water meets salt water, an electric current is created. British researchers have determined that the energy released when a river flows into the sea is as great as if this same river plunged over a 700-foot waterfall. No feasible way of capturing this staggering energy has yet been developed. However, at a laboratory level, researchers have created a battery which develops power when fresh and salt water are made to flow through alternate cells.

9. TAMING THE SEA

A hurricane comes roaring up out of the South Atlantic, threatening the mainland. Can meteorologists predict and chart the course of the tropical storm with complete accuracy? Can scientists find a way to stem its fury and break it up before it becomes a destroyer of life and property?

* * *

In the far Pacific, deep under the sea, an earthquake rocks the ocean floor. It sets in motion a seismic wave that races along at more than 400 miles an hour. Can science detect the wave when it starts and chart its course in time to give warning to people living on the shores it may batter?

* * *

Through the cold grey mist of the North Atlantic, a huge iceberg lumbers through the seas, moving directly toward the shipping lanes. Can watchers of the International Ice Patrol spot the white marauder that could so easily cause another *Titanic* disaster?

* * *

Scientists are seeking—and finding—the answers to these and other questions. The vast climatic and weather forces present in the sea are still beyond man's power to control, but scientists have made great strides toward understanding them and predicting their ways. New instruments, new techniques, and new co-operative enterprises involving many nations are being put to work to make the seas more usable to man.

Sea-borne menace—the hurricane

The violent, whirling storms called hurricanes are the targets of man's first efforts to tame the weather created at sea. A hurricane, which eventually may cover an area of thousands of square miles, begins as a comparatively small storm at sea. When its winds begin to set up a circular pattern around a low pressure area, the storm begins to grow and move slowly. As it moves, it grows in size and power until it becomes a roaring monster.

The United States has the world's most extensive hurricane warning system, a vast information-gathering network that keeps watch on the development and progress of these awesome sea storms. Scores of ground stations and hundreds of ships and aircraft turn in radio reports. From the National Hurricane Center in Miami, all information about hurricanes goes out over a teletype network to regional hurricane-forecast bases.

The most dramatic storm observations are made by the "hurricane patrol," a

The tremendous force of hurricane winds drove this piece of timber through the trunk of a palm tree.

1. Developing depression, June 5.

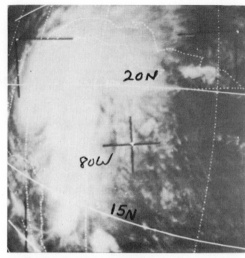

2. Tropical storm, June 6.

3. Hurricane entering Florida, June 9.

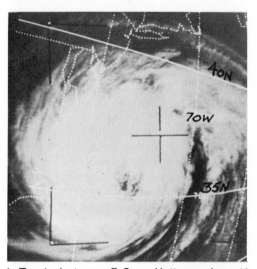

4. Tropical storm off Cape Hatteras, June 12.

Photos from a weather satellite show (1) an unnamed disturbance in the northwest Caribbean Sea; (2) the storm, now named "Alma," approaching hurricane force south of Cuba; (3) "Alma," a full-fledged hurricane, crossing the Florida panhandle; (4) the weakened storm heading out to sea off Cape Hatteras.

group of aircraft that flies right into the heart of the storms. These flying reconnaissance labs have a crew of 8 or 10, including a weather officer who sits in the nose of the plane where he can make direct personal observations. A number of instruments on the plane gather information about wind speeds, air pressure and other data that can best be obtained right in the midst of the storm itself. When the hurricane watchers fly above the storm, they can gather data by the use of a dropsonde, a small radio transmitter dropped by parachute. As it falls it sends back information about temperature, pressure and humidity.

Watchers in planes and at ground stations are able to obtain accurate large-scale pictures of a hurricane by the use of radar, which now has a range of about 200 miles. Improvements promise to extend this distance.

The most significant hurricane spotter is the all-seeing eye of the camera aboard a *Tiros* or *Nimbus* weather satellite. In April, 1960, a hurricane—or typhoon, as it is called in the Pacific—was roaring across the sea 800 miles east of Brisbane, Australia. It was still in a lonely stretch of ocean, so no one knew of its existence until a history-making event in weather forecasting took place.

In far-off Fort Monmouth, New Jersey, U.S. Weather Bureau scientists were analyzing photographs flashed back to earth from the satellite, *Tiros I*, when one of them uttered a startled exclamation.

"It's a hurricane!"

Sure enough, there, clearly identifiable, was the storm off Australia. A quick radio check with the Australian Meteorological Bureau revealed that they had no knowledge of the raging storm.

"This means that hurricanes spawned anywhere over vast oceanic areas can be detected much earlier than ever before possible," announced Dr. F. W. Reichelderfer, chief of the U.S. Weather Bureau. It was a prophecy which has since been borne out as other satellites have flashed warning pictures of numerous hurricanes.

Can hurricanes be stopped?

In the 1940's, scientists concluded that if clouds in hurricanes could be "seeded" with silver iodide particles, changes would occur in the storm. Supercooled water in the clouds might be changed to rain, as in experiments with man-made rain. Or, it was reasoned, the effects of seeding might increase the amount of energy concentrated in one part, breaking up the circular movement around the storm's eye or bringing about a change in its direction.

The first hurricane-stopping attempt was made in 1947, when U.S. Air Force planes seeded hurricane clouds off the coast of Georgia. The project was deemed a failure, as were others made later.

It was clear to the scientists that there must be a better way to seed clouds than just dumping chemicals from a hopper. Something was needed that would "sow" the silver iodide evenly along the flight track of the dispensing aircraft.

They found just the device they needed.

Dr. Pierre Saint Amand and his associates, at the U.S. Naval Ordnance Test Station, at China Lake, California, had developed a tiny but powerful gadget called the Alecto Generator. Just 3 inches in diameter and 8 inches long, it weighs only 7 pounds. This unit, loaded with 4 pounds of chemicals, is fired from the aircraft by a photoflash launcher. As it is launched, its chemicals ignite. The unit burns for about 40 seconds after being dropped from a height of 20,000 feet.

Project Stormfury

The Alecto Generator became the key to Project Stormfury, in which the U.S. Navy, Weather Bureau and Air Force and a panel of university scientists have joined forces. The experiment which launched Stormfury took place in 1961 when Hurricane Esther was moving towards the southern U.S.

A Navy A3B carrying Alecto Generators flew into the storm zone which scientists had selected as being the most promising to

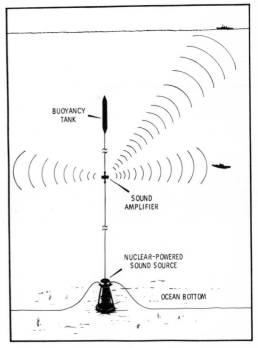

Although designed for military purposes, nuclear-powered ocean-floor buoys may serve as detectors of underwater disturbances related to the formation of seismic waves.

105

An engineer testing a model of a buoy which will be used to send back weather reports from the sea.

observed. On the following day, another attempt was made. Soon after the second seeding, observers reported that the pressure in the eye of the hurricane rose sharply, and that the strongest winds began to move away from the storm center. The hurricane was showing signs of breaking up.

Was it a result of the seeding? The cautious researchers could not be sure: "Natural oscillations within the hurricane, of which, as yet, little is known, could well have accounted for these changes," they reported.

In 1965, one of the major milestones in hurricane control was passed when Stormfury scientists struck at the cloud formations that play a part in the start of hurricanes. Between the period of July 28 and August 11, seeding planes roared into action against giant cumulus clouds gathering ominously in the Caribbean. They chose to make an attack on 12 clouds, while not molesting 7 others which would serve as controls.

They soon had striking evidence that they were accomplishing something. The 12 seeded clouds expanded rapidly, growing an average of 7,500 feet each. The energy in them was being dissipated. The unseeded control clouds? They expanded too, to be sure, but only at an average of 2,300 feet. The probability of the growth in the control clouds "being due to chance, is less than 1 in 1000," the researchers stated.

To be sure, these experiments had not stopped any actual storms, but they had demonstrated the power of seeding clouds that go into making a hurricane.

The terrible tsunami

Scientific progress has made a great advance in developing accurate forecasting of the dreaded "tidal wave." Scientists call this destructive phenomenon a "seismic wave"— or "tsunami," from the Japanese words for "harbor" and "wave."

It was the tsunami of April 1, 1946, which began off the Aleutian Islands, that led to the establishment of a complex tsunami warning system. On that morning, the northern Pacific ocean floor heaved and rolled in the successive shocks of a mighty earthquake. A vast chunk of ocean floor collapsed, leaving a huge hole, into which water rushed from all sides. On the surface,

attack. There the plane dropped 8 of the devices from an altitude of 43,000 feet. As the Alectos plunged downwards, through 4 miles of the storm path, they left a stream of silver iodide behind them. Less than 20 minutes afterwards, "notable changes" in the storm were indicated on the radar screens of the observing planes. The change, according to a report by an observing scientist, was "hard to explain unless it was due to the rapid transformation of supercooled liquid water to ice"—a result which silver iodide could bring about.

In another seeding effort, scientists estimated that winds in a storm were reduced 10 per cent. This experiment was labelled "interesting but inconclusive." However, the hurricane attacked did not do any damage, and some enthusiasts credited the seeding efforts.

In 1963, the Stormfury scientists turned their attention to Hurricane Beulah, a promising target which had moved into a position northeast of San Juan, Puerto Rico. On August 23, cloud-seeding generators were fired into the threatening storm. No effect was this created gigantic swells which then rushed outwards. Those travelling east, west and north soon crashed against nearby un-inhabited land. But the one moving south had no land mass to stop it. It rolled forward, an unbroken wave of water, perhaps 100 miles long, moving at a speed of 450 miles an hour. Only a little more than 4 hours later it was off the shore of the Hawaiian Islands, 2,500 miles away from the vortex near the Aleutians.

The wall of water that thundered on to Hawaii left a black wake of ruins around the rim of all 8 islands. From Hilo's Wailuku River it tore loose the railway bridge, tossed the heavy steel span aside to a spot nearly a thousand feet away. Railway cars, boats, houses and other buildings were tossed into heaps of debris. Hawaii counted its dead at 159 and set its damage at $25,000,000. Hundreds were injured and homeless.

Yet even this was a midget compared with some of the tsunamis that have slashed across oceans in the past. One of the biggest followed the Lisbon earthquake of 1755. Fifty feet high, the ocean poured in over the shattered city, then rushed away from it, forming a monster wave that crossed the sea to hit Atlantic shores as widely separated as those of England and the West Indies.

Another raging tsunami followed the volcanic explosion that blew apart the island of Krakatoa in the East Indies in 1883. The waves then may have reached the greatest of all recorded heights—over 100 feet—and smaller versions of them travelled through all the world ocean.

Though the tsunami can occur in any ocean, the most frequent playground is the Pacific. Hawaii is assailed on an average of once every 25 years and Japan has repeatedly been deluged by such catastrophic waves as the one in 1896 which killed 27,000 people.

For all its savagery in attacking shores, the tsunami has no record of destroying ships at sea. For, amazingly, a ship can sail right through the huge swell racing across the ocean without suffering any damage. Even more remarkable, those aboard the ship may not even know they have encountered this killer of the seas. For instance, in the great wave of 1896, fishermen from Japanese villages did not even interrupt their fishing when the wave went by. Their first knowledge

A U.S. Coast Guard aircraft tracking icebergs for the Ice Patrol. Most of the Patrol's recon-naissance is done from the air. Coast Guard cutters are called out only during bad weather, or when an iceberg drifts into shipping lanes and requires constant monitoring.

of the tsunami came when they returned that evening and looked with incredulous horror at the smashed remains of their homes.

The fact that the tsunami is a phantom at sea is explained by the great length of its wave in proportion to its size. The sailors in a ship that rises on a swell have no reference points at sea, and do not realize the change in their elevation. Moreover, the wave, which becomes so murderously powerful when it meets the obstacle of the shores, is com-paratively gentle in the vast expanse of the ocean.

Predicting the tsunami

Is there any way for science to fight the terrible force of the tsunami? That was the question leading oceanographers were asking themselves as, by coincidence, they were gathered in Hawaii, in preparation for atom bomb tests at Bikini, when they witnessed the 1946 April Fool wave. For the scientists, who had only read of this strange pheno-menon before, it was a shocking experience.

"What really bothered us," said Lieutenant Commander W. D. Patterson, superintendent of the Pacific Coast and Geodetic Survey, "was the fact that for hours the wave had been on its way—and yet it hit us without warning."

Dozens of scientists applied themselves to the problem, which seemed unbeatable. How could anyone find out when a tsunami started —and where it was going? True, any earthquake large enough to create a tsunami would register on seismographs, but only a few such earthquakes would actually create one. The inhabitants of all Pacific coasts could not be subjected to false alarms every time an earthquake rocked a part of the sea floor.

It was C. K. Green, a scientist of the Coast and Geodetic Survey, who hit on the answer, in the form of a remarkable wave gauge. Placed in the ocean, the gauge has a maze of pipes and cunning electronic circuits that ignore ordinary ocean waves. But let a tsunami wave tumble through the maze, and exact measurements will flash to indicators set up in a network of stations, all feeding their reports into prediction headquarters in Honolulu.

The device got its first test in 1952. One November morning seismographs in California, Alaska and Arizona all told the same story: A serious earthquake had occurred in the ocean at 51 degrees north latitude, 158 degrees east longitude. This information was quickly followed by news from Midway Island, where one of the Green devices was probing waves as they rolled past it. It told them a tsunami was on its way towards Hawaii.

Warnings were flashed to the civil authorities on the islands: Get people to high ground . . . take all steps to protect property at the water's edge.

The mighty waves came roaring in as the scientists had predicted they would. They thundered over shore homes, up across roadways. But movable property had been secured, the roads had been cleared of cars, people in close-to-shore houses had been evacuated to safe places.

When the waves at last receded, there was no tragic record of death and destruction. Damages were limited to less than $1,000,000, and not a single human life was lost!

The new warning system

In spite of successful predictions that have been made about many tsunamis since then, the ocean scientists are not satisfied with the limited warnings and are building a new and greatly improved system.

In addition to the 14 seismographic earthquake detectors that have been located in different places in the Pacific, the tsunami warning system will have at least 70 wave stations, in deep-sea locations. Unlike earlier wave indicators, these are being placed in deep water near known tsunami generating areas, rather than in ports and shallow water close to shore.

The deep-sea locations are made possible by new pieces of equipment. Among them is a telemetering buoy that reports wave conditions. In the buoy is a transducer which responds to changes in pressure and depth. It can sense a depth drop of less than .02 of a foot and transmit this information by wire to a surface float. The float contains a transmitter which radios the data to a control center in Honolulu, Tokyo or elsewhere. There the data can be processed by computers which give scientists an idea of just how big the waves will be, and just where they will strike. Prediction of wave height is particularly difficult because what starts out as a 2-foot wave at the site of an undersea upheaval may turn out to be 50 feet high when it reaches shore hundreds or thousands of miles away.

Icebergs

Far from tropical seas, science has declared war on another sea menace, the ice monsters which drift slowly across the North Atlantic shipping lanes. They are as much a danger to ships today as they were in 1912, when the *Titanic* on its maiden voyage struck one and sank almost immediately. Each year, it is estimated, 7,500 sizable bergs break off the thick glaciers along the coast of Greenland and start their long and menacing voyages southwards.

They usually spend the first winter of their floating lives in the vicinity of Melville Bay, Greenland. The next year, those that are still in existence move slowly westwards across

Damage to this iceberg from a 1,000-pound bomb was only slight. Several attempts to break up icebergs by bombing have been made by the Ice Patrol, but none of them have been very successful. Setting off dye bombs to stain icebergs bright red, so that they can be more easily tracked, has proved more efficient. They can be observed over a period of many weeks and their rate of drift and deterioration determined.

Baffin Bay to the Canadian Arctic coastline and spend a second winter a little farther south, around Cape Dyer. The following spring they start moving again, winding up a 3,000-mile trip near the Grand Banks off Newfoundland. As they edge into the Gulf Stream, where the water temperature rises to more than 60 degrees F., they begin to melt, a process which, because of the huge bulk of some bergs, may take as long as two weeks.

An average iceberg is 1,500 feet in length, with 300 feet above the water line. The U.S. Coast Guard Cutter *Eastwind* once observed an iceberg 550 feet above the water line. Since only about 1/10th of a berg's bulk is visible, it is not hard to figure that many big ones weigh over 1,500,000 tons. The number

actually reaching shipping lanes varies from year to year. Some seasons almost none are sighted; the record is 1,200 spotted in 1957.

Today's International Ice Patrol, set up in 1914 to keep track of icebergs and to study related ocean phenomena, has taken on an increasingly scientific character as it makes use of new technological advances. Though its work is delegated to the U.S. Coast Guard, the Patrol is a truly international organization that points the way toward possible multi-nation co-operation in the exploitation of sea riches. The Patrol is supported by 17 nations—Belgium, Canada, Denmark, France, Germany, Great Britain, Greece, Italy, Japan, Liberia, The Netherlands, Norway, Panama, Spain, Sweden, the United States, and Yugoslavia.

Another U.S. Coast Guard attempt at iceberg destruction. This small berg, off the coast of Newfoundland, has been coated with lamp black, the theory being that the carbon will catch the sun's heat and melt the iceberg.

Find the bergs!

The Patrol has turned over to aircraft some of the tasks once performed by Coast Guard cutters. Radar-equipped planes, flying mainly from the Patrol's iceberg-season base at Argentia, Newfoundland, fly criss-cross patterns across the 33,000-square-mile section of sea guarded by the Patrol. Though their record of spotting bergs is almost perfect, the word "almost" is troubling to the iceberg hunters. For one thing, radar has limitations in locating icebergs. It shows all objects, and it is often hard to tell whether a "blip" on the radar screen indicates a ship or a berg. For another, experts calculate that an iceberg is only 1/60th as efficient a radar reflector as a ship.

"When you get a ship and an iceberg close together—a dangerous situation—the berg may not show up at all," explains a Patrol flier.

The limitations of radar have meant that the flying patrolmen have had to depend on visual sightings, just as the cutters did in the days before radar.

What was needed was a device that could positively identify an iceberg under all conditions. The Patrol believes that it has such a device in the Radiometric Detector, devised by U.S. Coast Guard and Sperry engineers. The Detector is based on the principle that all matter sends out electromagnetic impulses. The intensity of the impulse emanating from an object depends on its composition, surface characteristics, temperature, and the amount of micro-wave energy in its surroundings. A metal ship emits a quite different amount of energy than an iceberg. The Radiometric Detector is operated in conjunction with the aircraft's radar system. While the radar scans ahead to search out objects for investigation, the Radiometric Detector studies the surface below and astern. The instrument screens in the aircraft reveal the sighted objects in outline form.

When an iceberg is detected, a Loran device is used to determine its exact location so that warnings can be issued to ships. Thereafter the Patrol keeps the berg in sight, both on instruments and visually.

In 1966, the Patrol began, on a large scale, a system of dyeing bergs. A calcium-chloride-rhodamine bomb, dropped from a low flying plane, splatters the berg with a bright vermilion dye which penetrates about an inch into the ice. Improved bombs dye the entire berg in this gaudy hue, unlike earlier experimental bombs which simply created a bright patch on part of the berg.

The Patrol is working on teaming satellite photo reconnaissance with computers to keep track of icebergs. More than that, however, scientists hope to predict the course of icebergs with precision. This would be particularly valuable during periods when the shipping lanes are shrouded in dense fog.

From time to time, the Patrol has tried to destroy icebergs, but, so far, can report little success. Icebergs have been thermite bombed, mined with demolition charges, and bombarded by gunfire. All the bombing has made hardly a dent on the icy surfaces. Admiral W. J. Smith, Commandant of the U.S. Coast Guard, says that breaking up a medium-sized berg would require almost 400,000 pounds of TNT.

Why not melt the icebergs? That's impossible, too, he claims. Melting an average iceberg would demand the heat generated by

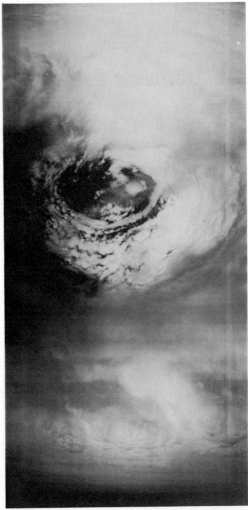

The eye of hurricane Betsy, Sept., 1965, photographed from a U.S. Air Force plane. The towering "eyewall" is at the top of the picture.

the combustion of 2,400,000 gallons of gasoline!

"Accurate prediction is our best objective," says the Admiral.

10. NEW FRONTIERS OF SEA KNOWLEDGE

Excavate sunken cities under the sea? Learn to talk to sea creatures and command them to do our bidding? Adapt the human organism so that it will be able to breathe water through artificial gills?

Science has made a firm start toward realizing these possibilities, and many others equally remarkable, which may well represent the most bountiful harvest of the sea—new knowledge and experiences to enrich our future.

Exploring the seas

The whole World Ocean may be said to be one vast frontier of science. With less than 5 per cent of the ocean floor accurately mapped, with only a small part of the sea's surface ever visited by ships, finding better ways to search the seas for knowledge is one of the greatest challenges to oceanology. Science has the instruments to probe the seas, but these versatile tools must somehow be towed or taken to remote parts of the seas. (Even the new research submersibles, valuable as they are in plunging beneath the surface, must be carried to the site of their exploration by mother ships.) The design of new kinds of oceanographic vessels to take the instruments to the farthest seas is, in itself, a challenge.

The slim white ship that slid down the greased ways at Jacksonville, Florida, on a bright April day in 1966, is a striking example of the new breed of floating laboratories. The *Oceanographer*, one of a fleet of 14 ships of the Environmental Sciences Services Administration (ESSA) of the U.S. Department of Commerce, is built to sustain a crew of 39, plus 50 or more scientists, at sea for 150 days at a time.

Oceanographer is constructed to operate with ease in any area of the global sea, including the ice-strewn waters of the Arctic and Antarctic. A bow thruster of 400 horsepower, located in a transverse tunnel through the ship's hull, enables the vessel to maintain a constant heading at low speeds despite wind and wave conditions.

Though not quite so large as the world's biggest oceanographic vessel—the U.S.S.R.'s *Mikhail Lomonsov*, which has accommodations for 65 scientists—the *Oceanographer* can lay claim to being the most modern and complete research ship afloat. She carries a complete range of seeing and sensing instruments, but the most remarkable piece of the ship's equipment is a computer. As the ship moves through the water, towed sensors feed their information into the computer, which records all data.

Technicians operating a giant crane on board the research ship "*Oceanographer*."

FLIP (Floating Instrument Platform) is a revolutionary research vessel developed at Scripps Institution of Oceanography. FLIP has no motive power of her own. She is towed in this horizontal position to the place where research is to be conducted, and "flipped" to a vertical position.

In the past, the researcher, after returning from a long voyage, was faced with the formidable task of sorting and analyzing data acquired at sea. The *Oceanographer's* Data Acquisition System records, sorts out, and analyzes the readings continuously.

While *Oceanographer* follows the lines of conventional ships, ocean scientists have designed a new class of radically different craft. First, and most famous of them, is FLIP, a vessel that really flips, classed as an "Underwater Instrument Platform." De-

FLIP in the process of "flipping" from a horizontal to a vertical position. This is accomplished by flooding her long aft section with sea water. To return FLIP to a horizontal position, high-pressure air blows the water out of the submerged section.

FLIP in its vertical "working" position. Only its bow section remains above the water. FLIP is now an extremely stable platform on which four scientists can live and conduct oceanographic studies. The scientists can descend 150 feet below the water in two watertight tubes inside FLIP's submerged section.

veloped by the Marine Physical Laboratory of the University of California's Scripps Institution of Oceanography, it enables sea-going scientists to realize an old dream. For FLIP combines the stability of a fixed platform with the mobility of a ship.

The idea for FLIP took shape in the minds of the Marine Physical Lab scientists when they needed a craft suitable for underwater acoustic work. Nothing in existence in the early 60's was exactly right. Scientists needed to get their instruments down in quiet underwater, away from the "noise" of surface waves. In calm weather, oceanographic ships were all right, but they were too unstable in rough weather. Submarines, which could be used, were much too expensive to build and operate. Why not, asked the scientists, headed by Dr. Fred N. Spies, build a craft that would be part submarine, part surface ship?

FLIP was the answer. Sometimes her 355-foot length floats in the water like any other ship. When she goes into operation as a research vessel, however, she flips until she looks like, as one scientist described her, "a fence post floating upright."

With no motive power of her own, FLIP is towed, in a horizontal position, to the area where she is to be flipped. The tow line is cast off, and the FLIP crew turn the valves that let 1,500 tons of sea water into ballast tanks that occupy 85 per cent of the space in the ship. As these tanks fill with water, the prow rises and the stern sinks. Soon only 55 feet of FLIP's length is above water. The water ballasted 300 feet below the surface enables her to stand straight and solid, hardly moving. In the face of the 35-foot waves that slammed at her in the Gulf of Alaska, scientists reported that her vertical oscillation was less than three inches!

The upper working portion of FLIP is divided into four floors. The first, or "top," contains berths for the crew of six; the second, an electronics laboratory; the third, galley and mess facilities for crew and scientific personnel, which may total as many as 15. The fourth and lowest is the engineer-

A FLIP type research station developed by Jacques-Yves Cousteau.

ing compartment, housing three diesel generators for auxiliary power, a master gyro compass, switchboards, lubricating oil tanks and diesel fuel tanks. Inside the circular hull are four more levels which were not part of the original design. They have been fitted up to provide additional living and laboratory space.

While crafts like *Oceanographer* and FLIP speed up the search for ocean knowledge, they are too costly to permit building by the dozen. This was the complaint of Dr. Sidney S. Galler, head of the Oceanic Biology Branch of the Office of Naval Research, U.S. Navy.

"We'll just never get enough oceanographic ships," he said, voicing an uncomfortable truth that had disturbed many scientists. "What we need," he added, "is *hundreds* of ships."

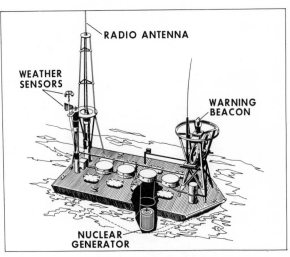

The first nuclear-powered deep-sea weather station, NOMAD, now operating unattended in the Gulf of Mexico. The station transmits weather data every three hours.

Dr. Galler, fortunately for the advancement of ocean science, did not stop with an expression of regret. He thought of a way to get literally hundreds of ships. His idea emerged as Project Neptune, an oceanographic research scheme that turns ordinary freighters and passenger ships into floating laboratories. Thanks to the host of new automatic oceanographic instruments that are able to take readings from moving ships, the scientists were able to develop Sea Van, an assemblage of instruments which can be hoisted on to the deck of any craft. Manned by one or two oceanographers, the 7-ton portable lab is equipped to take a variety of observations in any aspect of ocean phenomena.

Phase 1 of Project Neptune was conducted in the Pacific in the late summer of 1964 when the S.S. *Java Mail* of the American Mail Lines carried a Sea Van from Seattle to Hong Kong. It proved the feasibility of what is sometimes called RSO, "Research Ships of Opportunity."

In 1965, the project was conducted in the Atlantic when the *Export Champion*, of the American Export Isbrandtsen Lines, carried the mobile laboratory van from New York City to Mediterranean ports. The van was equipped with a "jet net," specially developed for the project. This net gathered plankton, live and in good condition, while the ship travelled at its full speed of 19 knots.

The Office of Naval Research announces that "it is planned to utilize the experience gained in designing compact mobile laboratories that can be placed on any ocean-going ship, including passenger liners, to gather data as the ships cruise to all parts of the world. With the purchase of cabin space for the scientists the only major expense of the voyage, it is anticipated that a great amount of biological information about the oceans of the world can be obtained at modest expense."

Monitoring the world ocean

Oceanographic ships, no matter how advanced and no matter how many are put into operation cannot provide scientists with all the information they need about the sea. To fully understand the World Ocean and its possibilities oceanologists must find a way to get continuous hour-by-hour reports, from every part of the sea.

Today, oceanologists have the three basic tools that will make it possible to monitor the world's oceans. Two of them—space satellites and computers—have been developed primarily for use in other fields, but can be adapted to the needs of ocean science.

The third component of the team, the telemetering buoy, is a product of the combined efforts of oceanographers and engineers. A few years ago the Office of Naval

The extensive computer system at Scripps Institution of Oceanography. Such installations can be linked to telemetering buoys at sea.

Research invited leading oceanographers to outline their specifications for a buoy which could be placed anywhere in the ocean to make and transmit automatic readings of sea conditions.

The scientists promptly came back with a set of specifications that gave engineers a challenging assignment. The buoy, they said, must have:

Designed as a navigational aid, this study buoy is adaptable as a telemetering device to monitor sea conditions. It is capable of withstanding storm waves and hurricane winds.

1. At least 100 sensors for acquisition of both oceanographic and atmospheric data.
2. A scanning system that would take readings on all sensors at least once an hour.
3. Telemetering apparatus capable of transmitting the stored data from the sensors upon command from a shore station, perhaps 2,500 miles away.
4. A long-term memory system in which all data could be stored for one year.

It is a triumph for ocean science that, by 1967, such a buoy had actually been created by engineers of the General Dynamics Company. A huge, discus-shaped device, it is 40 feet in diameter. Jutting up from it is a 32-foot-high mast which supports a large antenna. Inside the buoy are housed the radio transmitter, power sources, and magnetic tape recorders. To the mooring line, or anchor cable, which holds the buoy in place, are attached electrical sensors capable of taking measurements of water temperature, current direction, salinity, and many other important data. These transmit their readings to the receiving apparatus in the buoy, which in turn stores it on tape. On receiving an impulse from a land station, the tape plays off its message for immediate use by the shore lab. The recording then becomes part of the

A computerized system of global weather prediction is tried out at the U.S. Weather Bureau's Research Lab. (1) The global weather data is analyzed, (2) then it is transferred to punched cards to feed the computer, (3) a mathematician outlines the computer's program, (4) the computer gives its forecast after processing the data.

permanent memory bank, awaiting scientists who make periodic trips to the buoy.

Scientists look forward to the day when a network of these versatile buoys will monitor the seas. Strategically placed, they would report on water temperature, changes in currents, height of waves and variations in the chemical composition of sea water. They would provide a detailed supplement to information picked up by the cameras and radar aboard satellites. Fed to shore-based computers, the combined data will make possible accurate long-range weather and fishery condition forecasts.

Weather prediction and control

Probably the first use of the satellite-buoy-computer combination will be in an integrated system of weather reporting. Let Captain E. T. Harding, Assistant Director of the U.S. Naval Weather Service, give his picture of such a system, which he predicts will be in operation by the mid-70's, or sooner:

"In the stratosphere there will be half a dozen weather satellites. There will be constant-level balloons to outline the wind flow at certain fixed pressure levels. In remote areas, over land and sea, there will be automatic weather stations. As the satellites pass overhead, the balloons and automatic weather stations will be interrogated and their reports stored on tape.

"The satellite meanwhile will be taking observations of its own. Again, at fixed points, the satellites will be interrogated by ground stations. At extremely high speeds the stored weather reports will feed to a computer at the read-out station. This computer

The research submersible "*Asherah's*" headlight pierces the sunless ocean depths. This submarine has proved a valuable tool for underwater archaeologists.

will automatically . . . relay the data to a master computer for processing and storage on memory tape.

"At set intervals, perhaps an hour, perhaps more, the computer will add the collection of reports to those used for the last weather and oceanographic analysis. The computer will bring all the charts—surface, upper-air and oceanographic—up to date. Forecasts of all types will be available for periods of from hours to days ahead, with accuracies almost perfect for shorter periods; and for periods up to 30 days we might expect accuracies superior to what we now have for 24 hours. The computers will have great versatility in reaction to forecast demands. We will be able to ask them to forecast winds over an aircraft route 10 days from now, the state of the sea at a specified point at 12 hour intervals for the next four days, or anything we want in the way of prognostication.

"The satellites will report all potential severe tropical and extra-tropical cyclones to

the computers, which will pass on the word to the weatherman. He, in turn, will decide whether to modify the cyclone, and if so, how much—probably just enough so the cyclones will not imperil life and property, but not so much as to interfere with climatic factors. The computers will keep posting situation reports on weather conditions all over the world. The reports will include the status of rainfall, overheating, overcooling, air pollution. forest fires and damaging winds. They will include notification of weather patterns suitable for modification . . . Then, based on computer calculations, we might increase or decrease rainfall, sunshine, winds —whatever might be needed for an area of trouble."

There is no question that we have moved very close to realization of the dream of made-to-order weather. Without our growing fund of information about the ways of the world's great heat engine and weather breeder, the World Ocean, we could not have hoped to challenge the weather.

Underwater archaeology

June 7, 1692, started just like any other day in the bustling city of Port Royal. Sailing into the port came ships bearing raw materials from the New World and finished goods from the capitals of Europe, for Port Royal was the focal point of Caribbean activity and capital of the important British colony of Jamaica. But sometime during midday the busy routine of Port Royal was suddenly shattered. The ground heaved and cracked open and people ran screaming through the streets. Great crevices opened in the land and buildings toppled. Then, just as suddenly, a huge tidal wave roared in from the sea, smashing the boats in port and engulfing the city.

When the earthquake subsided, the glory that was Port Royal was no more. Two-thirds of the city lay beneath the sea and thousands of people lay in watery graves.

Much of what happened that day in 1692, however, was not to be known until nearly three centuries later, when in 1959, the new science of underwater archaeology made reconstruction of Port Royal possible. With the invention of new equipment, archaeologists are now able to leave the land, where their discoveries have long been of invaluable aid to historians, and enter into the timeless world of the sea where, waiting to be unraveled, lie countless mysteries in the form of sunken ships and lost cities.

The first step toward making underwater archaeology a practical science was made when Jacques-Yves Cousteau developed the aqualung. This light-weight, self-contained underwater breathing apparatus (SCUBA) freed the diver from the clumsy, as well as dangerous, diving suit and helmet. The underwater archaeologist could now move around his site with almost as much ease as his landlubber colleague.

Another important device followed soon after the aqualung—the so-called "airlift." This consists of a large flexible tube through which a powerful jet of water sucks up material from the ocean floor. Aboard the research vessel, the material is sifted through screens and valuable objects are carefully collected.

A more sophisticated technique now used in the study of ancient sunken ships is that

Captain Cousteau examines a treasure from the deep. Underwater archaeology is yielding many finds like this vase, which dates from 240 B.C.

of laying out an extensive iron gridwork over the entire wreck. After this is done, the archaeologists carefully photograph and label every object, down to each bit of broken pottery, indicating exactly where it was found, before anything is brought to the surface. In this way there is a permanent record that scientists can study for years afterwards. From these studies, our knowledge of the ancient Greeks and Romans and other sea-roving peoples will continue to grow.

New tools are being used in the search for sunken vessels as well as in their salvage. An electronic device called a magnetometer can locate objects on the sea floor. Induction detectors which record the presence of metal are used to survey an underwater site in greater detail.

Possibly the greatest boon to the underwater archaeologist is the development of small submersibles. One such sub, called *Asherah*, specially designed for wreck surveying and excavating, can hold two men and remain at a site for as long as ten hours.

Not only science has gained from the discoveries beneath the waves, but art as well. Some of our finest pieces of Greek statuary have come from wreck sites at Antikythera and Mahdia in the Mediterranean Sea.

The startling nature of some of the finds is well demonstrated by an incident at the Port Royal excavation. One of the many objects brought up by the airlift was an uninteresting looking lump of metal that was at first passed over. When it was finally examined it was found to be a watch, the hands of which were stopped at 17 minutes to 12, quite probably the exact time of the earthquake.

There are many other cities like Port Royal awaiting the adventurous archaeologist of tomorrow. Just recently a team of Greek scientists discovered what appears to be the ancient Greek city of Helice, destroyed in 373 B.C. in much the same fashion as Port Royal.

Perhaps the biggest question in the back of every archaeologist's mind is one that people have argued over for centuries: Is there a lost continent of Atlantis? Recent re-interpretations of the Atlantis myth have led scientists to believe that Atlantis may in fact be the once-great civilization of Minoan Crete, which flourished long before the Golden Age of Greece and disappeared suddenly in a terrible disaster—probably a massive volcanic eruption. So, somewhere beneath the sea near the island of Crete, Atlantis may lie preserved in a watery museum, waiting for the first underwater archaeologist lucky enough to find it.

Putting dolphins to work

A diver was lost in the murky depths of the Pacific Ocean off the west coast of the United States near San Diego. Visibility at his depth was about 10 feet. He waited, almost motionless, filled with doubt. He had been told that a 7-foot bottle-nosed dolphin (or porpoise) named Tuffy would find him and lead him back to the undersea chamber where he temporarily lived and worked with other men in the U.S. Navy's man-in-the-sea program.

Then suddenly there was Tuffy, brushing against the diver, almost affectionately it seemed. He wore a plastic harness to which was attached a nylon rope. Following the dolphin's lead, the diver was soon inside the chamber, sipping a cup of coffee and telling fellow scientists about Tuffy's performance.

Training a marine creature to find a lost diver is but one example of scientific experiments aimed at making the dolphin a partner of man-in-the-sea—a guide, messenger boy and fellow worker. Scientists are sure that there will be many others like Tuffy, who has been taught by U.S. Navy researchers to perform such undersea tasks as carrying slates on which messages are written, delivering tools, and locating lost equipment that has fallen to the sea floor.

In their work with dolphins, scientists have learned to respect this highly intelligent sea creature. The dolphin is an air-breathing, warm-blooded mammal with a body temperature about the same as our own. He (or she) has a brain that is bigger, and in some ways more complex, than man's. He has a personality which makes him an ideal underwater co-worker with man, for he is friendly, co-operative and seems to enjoy human companionship.

His underwater movements are far more

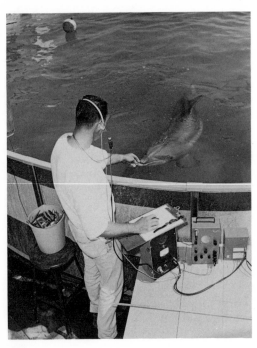

A scientist at the U.S. Naval Marine Biology Facility, Point Mugu, California, conducts a test with a porpoise. Such tests contribute valuable information to man-in-the-sea experimentation.

Tuffy the porpoise leaps for a reward after performing well in tests with "*Sealab II*" aquanauts.

skilfully executed than those of a human diver outfitted with the best that science can provide. For the dolphin is equipped with a built-in sonar superior to anything man has yet developed. In opaque water a dolphin can identify and locate objects many feet away.

"So sensitive is his auditory system," reports Dr. W. N. Kellogg, of Florida State University, referring to experiments conducted in a large tank, "that it can hear a single BB shot dropped into the water, or half a teaspoonful of water dropped from a height of 5 or 6 feet. When an object such as a fish is dropped into the water, the noise of the splash provokes a torrent of sputtering sound pulses as the dolphins dash toward the target."

The dolphin's auditory apparatus includes a scanning system. As a dolphin swims forward, he makes a clicking sound while sweeping his head back and forth. Returning echoes point the direction of prey or predator, or any object he has been trained to locate. The interval between sending and receiving tells the dolphins the distance to the object, while variations in the echo-sound reveal its size and nature.

Extending man's undersea powers

A diver picks up a machine that weighs over 1,000 pounds and strides across the sea floor with it.

Fantastic? Not at all. In many research laboratories, engineers are at work devising equipment that will permit not only longer stays beneath the water, but greater use of the diver's time on the sea floor.

Hardiman, for example, is a device which permits a diver to perform superhuman feats. Developed by the U.S. Office of Naval Research, its name stands for "Human Augmentation Research and Development Investigation," after the ONR's project designation. It is a powered, exo-skeleton suit, or structure, which gives an ordinary man the power of a giant.

By means of a complicated system of control linkages and servo-mechanisms, this unique machine will mimic and amplify the movements of its wearer, dramatically extending his strength and endurance. It combines the operator's dexterity, brain power and all-around versatility with a machine's strength, size and ruggedness.

121

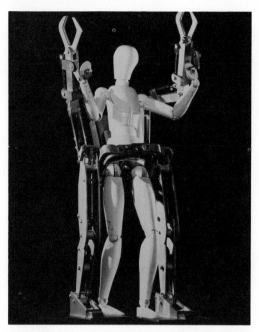

"Hardiman"—a set of "mechanical muscles" which allow a person to lift 1,500 pounds while exerting only 40 pounds of force. The machine is attached to the operator's feet, forearms, and waist, enabling him to perform a great variety of load-handling tasks, such as those necessary in underwater salvage.

Worn like an external skeleton, the structure permits the man who wears it to lift a 1,500-pound load. He can easily raise it to a height of 6 feet, where he can hold it for 30 seconds, or carry it, at that height, for a distance of 25 feet in 10 seconds.

In another area of development, engineers are seeking to put nuclear power to use for undersea workers. One application is a new kind of heated diving suit that will permit divers to work all day in the coldest water. The heat is provided by a nuclear device carried at the diver's waist. The fuel is radioactive thulium isotopes 170 and 171, which, as they decay, give off energy that is used to heat a closed cycle supply of distilled water. A pump circulates this water through a flexible, tube-lined undergarment worn next to the skin. The diver can control the temperature of the water by turning a knob mounted on top of the power unit.

The isotopes also power a small generator

which produces 5 watts of electrical power. This solves another problem of working underwater. In the murky depths it is often hard for divers to find each other. The electricity from the generator is used to operate a powerful xenon gas lamp, which flashes on and off every second. It serves as a beacon for fellow divers. The light is visible, even in dark water, at a distance of 100 feet.

The nuclear unit provides full power for a period as long as two years without renewal of the isotopes. Though the compact little power packet weights 35 pounds, this is no handicap to the diver because it replaces some of the ballast and trim weights necessary in a diving suit. The diver is so well shielded from the radiation that he could wear the suit for months at a time without danger.

Another extension of man's undersea capabilities is coming in the form of new tools for underwater use. A striking example of new ventures in this field is the "hand held object locator," developed by the technicians of the Navy Electronics Laboratory in San Diego. It is a battery-operated, self-contained device which transmits ultrasonic signals and detects the presence of objects by their reflected echoes. It is buoyant in sea water, and is easily controlled by diver or swimmer.

The object locator is used like a searchlight, except that it "sees" by sound; that is, it transmits audible signals instead of visual ones. The diver points the acoustic beam in the direction that interests him. If the sound beam hits an object, the diver will hear a humming sound that warns him that something solid is ahead. The range of the object locator is far beyond that of the diver's sight. It operates as well in murky water as in clear. As operators become more skilled in its use, they can interpret the reflected sound and gain some idea of just what kind of object is sending it back—an undersea creature, a coral reef, or a sunken ship.

Homo aquaticus

Man's exploration and use of the abundant and fascinating world beneath the waves has always been limited by need for vital oxygen, the gas that sustains life as we know it. Divers carry their supply of air with them as they plunge into the sea. But new developments in science seem to point to a day when men

Remotely controlled robots may further extend man's powers under the sea.

might be able to inhale oxygen directly from sea water itself. Researchers around the world are busy exploring this.

Waldemar Ayres, an inventor from Rutherford, New Jersey, thought he could make a synthetic "gill" that would do for men what the living tissues of fishes' gills do. Ayres found that modern chemistry had created many materials—plastics such as polystyrenes and rubber silicones—which would let oxygen through and keep water out. Air has, on the average, 200 milliliters of oxygen to every liter of air—approximately 20 per cent. Sea water contains only about 9 milliliters of what scientists know as "dissolved oxygen" to every liter of water. The percentage is small —only about 1.1 per cent. Was this enough oxygen to supply a man's needs?

Ayres answered his questions at New York's Jones Beach. While bathers watched curiously, Ayres waded out into the water, carrying a weird assemblage of plastic sheets hooked together by rubber hosing such as divers use.

Out in the water, Ayres checked his equipment. On the bottom of each plastic sheet was a layer of "permeable membrane," one of the materials that would pass oxygen but not water. If his plan worked, oxygen from the sea water would slip through the membrane into the space between the two sheets. His system of rubber hosing, which

connected these spaces, would let him inhale the oxygen. When he exhaled, the carbon dioxide from his lungs would pass through the membrane out into the water. The floating "gills" rested quietly on the surface of the water as Ayres put his mouth over the aperture in the hosing and dunked his face beneath the water. An experienced scuba diver, he was used to being underwater, but this time he was filled with a new exhilaration as the minutes passed. He was breathing easily through his mouth and felt no sense of oxygen lack. His "gills" were working. For an hour and a half he remained in his position, breathing the oxygen from the sea itself!

Meanwhile Dr. Johannes A. Kylstra, of the State University of New York, in Buffalo, had proved that the mammalian lung is capable of extracting oxygen from water, as it ordinarily does from air. In his experiments, Dr. Kylstra used saline water to which oxygen had been added. Placing mice in tanks of such water, pressurized to several atmospheres (1 atmos.=14.7 lbs/sq. in.), he was able to keep them alive for long periods. The pressure and the extra oxygen enabled their lungs to function as gills. In another experiment, Dr. Kylstra used a dog as his subject. This mongrel mascot of a Dutch vessel emerged frisky and unharmed after 23 minutes of water-breathing. By applying Dr. Kylstra's discoveries, it might be possible for a deep-sea diver to breathe a liquid solution. He could carry with him a container of liquid salt solution, a heating element to keep it warm, and a small tank of compressed oxygen. The advantages of breathing a liquid, instead of a gas, lie in the fact that compressed gases can cause bubbles in the blood and necessitate long periods of decompression.

The final step toward making men underwater creatures is visualized by Jacques-Yves Cousteau.

"The departure yet to come," he says, "is the development of the new man—*Homo aquaticus*—by surgical means. When and if it is done, *Homo aquaticus* will be able to resist pressures down to 1,500 metres, and will be able to move from the surface to this great depth mechanically or freely, then return to the surface just as quickly with no decompression problem at all."

Cousteau bases his prediction on experiments made by doctors working in the field of space medicine. To prepare men for long journeys in space, they have developed the concept of circulating blood through a regenerative cartridge, which would restore its oxygen chemically, rather than through the astronaut's breathing process.

If these experiments are successful, they will make possible underwater living for men, free of the need for air breathing.

"Then," says Cousteau, "a whole new generation of man will be born, perhaps even in underwater hospitals, where, upon birth, infants will be operated upon . . . But this new species of man will not be confined to underwater. After surgery, he will be perfectly able to walk on land, still with the regenerating cartridge, changing it from time to time. The new man will be equally at home skiing on an Alpine slope or swimming in a submarine canyon."

An undersea workboat of a type expected to play a part in mineral extraction from the sea floor. The structure below the workboat is a habitat for undersea workers.

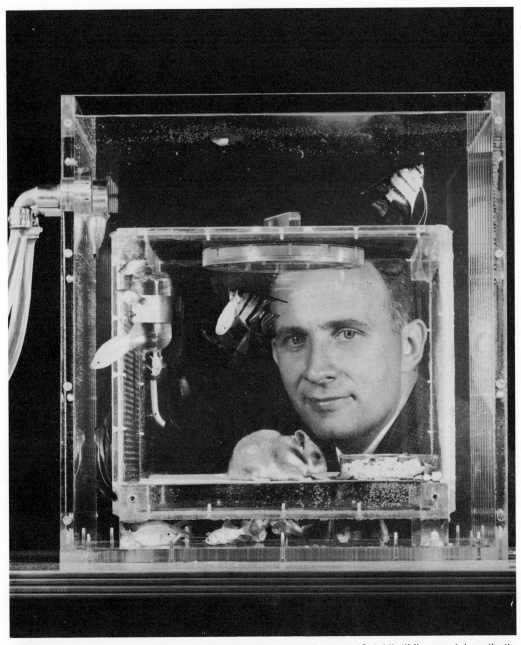

A hamster penned in a submerged plastic tank is kept alive by an artificial "gill," a special synthetic membrane stretched across the top, bottom and two sides of his underwater home. The gill extracts air from the surrounding water. Inventor of the membrane, Dr. Walter L. Robb, of G.E. Research and Development Center, is shown behind the tank.

INDEX